Year 11

MODULAR SCIENCE

for AQA

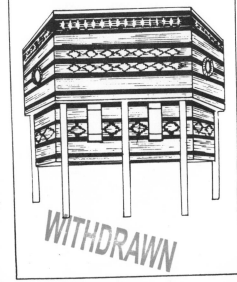

In usum scholarum
Scholae Regiae
Gippesvicensis

WITHDRAWN

Heinemann

Year 11

MODULAR SCIENCE

for AQA

Keith Hirst
Mike Hiscock
David Sang
Martin Stirrup

Heinemann

Heinemann Educational Publishers
Halley Court, Jordan Hill, Oxford OX2 8EJ
Part of Harcourt Education Limited

Heinemann is the registered trademark of
Harcourt Education Limited

© Keith Hirst, Mike Hiscock, David Sang and Martin Stirrup, 2002

First published 2002

06 05 04 03
10 9 8 7 6 5 4 3 2

ISBN 0 435 57205 9

British Library Cataloguing in Publication Data is available from
the British Library on request.

Edited by Patrick Bonham

Index compiled by Paul Nash

Original illustrations © Harcourt Education Limited, 2002

Illustrated, designed and produced by Hardlines Ltd,
Charlbury, Oxford

Printed in Spain by Edelvives

Acknowledgements
Every effort has been made to contact copyright holders of
material reproduced in this book. Any omissions will be rectified
in subsequent printings if notice is given to the publishers.

Picture research by Thelma Gilbert

SPL = Science Photo Library

Cover photos: Coloured flames SPL/Charles D. Winters;
Laboratory technician SPL/Geoff Tompkinson; Gyroscope ride
Corbis/Joseph Sohm.

T = top   B = bottom   R = right   L = left   M = middle

p3 T SPL, **M** Anthony Blake; **p5** SPL; **p6 T** SPL, **M** Roger Scruton;
p7 SPL; **p10 T** SPL, **B** SPL; **p12** Popperfoto; **p13** NHS; **p14** SPL; **p16**
SPL; **p18 T** Roger Scruton, **M** Anthony Blake; **p22 TL** Anthony
Blake, **TR** Anthony Blake, **M** Anthony Blake, **B** Rex Features; **p24 T**
Anthony Blake, **M** Anthony Blake, **B** Roger Scruton; **p25** Anthony
Blake; **p26 T** Anthony Blake, **B** Anthony Blake; **p27** Anthony Blake;
p29 SPL; **p30 TL** Robert Harding, **TR** Panos Pictures; **p32 TL** Rex
Features, **TR** Impact Photos, **M** Robert Harding, **B** Impact Photos;
p39 SPL; **p40** SPL; **p42** Peter Gould; **p44 all** Peter Gould; **p47**
Robert Harding; **p48 T** Robert Harding, **M** Trip Photos; **p49** Robert
Harding; **p52** AutoExpress; **p53 T** Elizabeth Whiting and
Associates, **M** Rex Features; **p54 T** Rex Features, **B** SPL; **p55** Peter
Gould; **p58** SPL; **p60 T** SPL, **M** Ann Ronan Picture Library; **p61 T**
Ann Ronan Picture Library, **M** SPL; **p64** SPL; **p68 T** SPL, **M** BBC, **B**
SPL; **p69 both** Rex Features; **p75** Rex Features; **p76 T** Christie's
Images, **M** Rex Features; **p77** Empics; **p78** Rex Features; **p80** The
Wellcome Trust; **p82 T** Ann Ronan Picture Library, **B** SPL; **p83**
Colorsport; **p85** Rex Features; **p86** Sporting Pictures (UK); **p87**
Peter Gould; **p88** SPL; **p92 T** Mary Evans, **M** Geo-Science Features;
p94 Mary Evans; **p97** Rex Features.

The publishers have made every effort to trace the copyright
holders, but if they have inadvertently overlooked any, they will be
pleased to make the necessary arrangements at the first opportunity.

Tel: 01865 888058 www.heinemann.co.uk

About this book

This book has been written for use alongside the AQA Modular Higher year 11 book. It covers everything you need to pass your module tests for:

◆ AQA Modular GCSE Biology
◆ AQA Modular GCSE Chemistry
◆ AQA Modular GCSE Physics

We have named each module in the book with the title of the module test that you will be set. This is so that you can be sure of what you need to study.

The introductory page to each module will help you get a feel of the module. It explains the topics covered in the module and gets you thinking about the science that you already know.

To help you study we have included some useful features in the book. Here are a few:

Mind maps
Each module has a mind map. You can use these to plan your way through the concepts that you will meet in the module. You may also find this helpful as a revision aid.

Double-page spreads
Everything you need to know for each module is covered in double-page spreads. These pages will cover all the topics you need to understand for your module tests, including recap material for Year 10 modules. To help you find all of the important points, we have included questions to test yourself as you learn.

End of module questions
These questions are similar to the type of questions you will find in your end of module tests. Answering lots of questions will help you check what you have learnt and prepare for the tests.

Extended homework questions
These questions are written to give you an opportunity to really get to grips with the ideas that have been covered in the module.

Summary
The information in these boxes summarises the most important points on the page. In your module tests you will be tested on your knowledge of the points in the summary boxes. These boxes will also help you make notes and answer questions.

Glossary pages
When a new scientific word appears for the first time in the text, it will appear in **bold** type. All words in **bold** are listed with their meanings in the glossary at the back of the book. Look there to remind yourself what they mean.

Contents

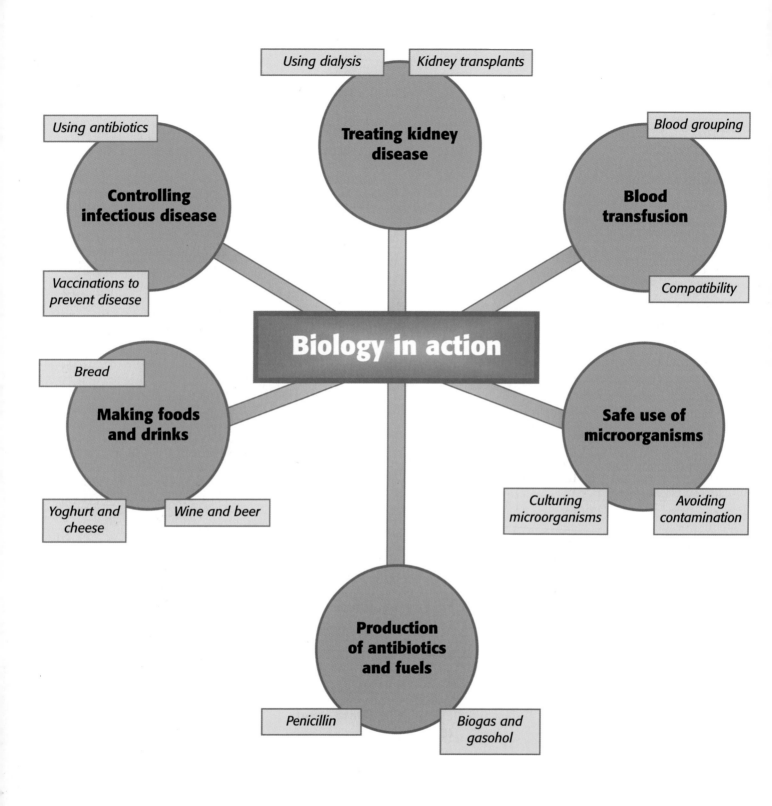

Module 20 – Biology in action

Harmful microorganisms

Many diseases are caused by bacteria and viruses. These microorganisms can be spread from an infected person to someone else. This is why such diseases are called **infectious diseases**. Your body's immune system protects you if you are infected, but some diseases can make you very ill. Doctors may also help you to recover using medicines such as **antibiotics**. You are protected against some diseases because you were **vaccinated** against the disease when you were younger.

Sometimes a disease or an accident damages an organ so that it stops working. This can make a person very ill and require regular treatment or even surgery to remove the damaged organ and replace it with a donated organ.

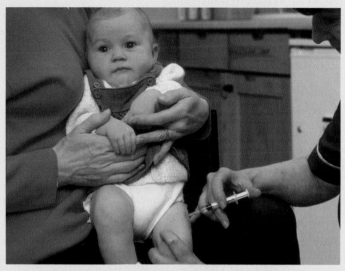

Vaccination can provide lifelong protection against disease.

Useful microorganisms

Not all microorganisms are harmful. Some are used to make useful products, including food, drinks, fuel and medicines. Cheese, yoghurt, bread, wine and beer are all made using microorganisms. Antibiotics to kill harmful microorganisms are made by useful microorganisms. In some countries even cars are run on fuel produced using microorganisms.

Not all microorganisms are harmful. This bread is made using yeast.

Before you start, check what you remember about microorganisms and disease.

1　Give two examples of infectious diseases that you have been vaccinated against.

2　As well as antibiotics, give two examples of other medicines that are used to help people recover from an infection. How do these medicines help recovery?

3　Biogas is a fuel produced by the action of microorganisms on animal faeces. Explain two advantages of using this fuel in a developing country.

This report followed an outbreak of meningitis. This is a very serious disease caused by bacteria passed from person to person. Fortunately, doctors soon had the outbreak under control and cases like this are rare. This is because doctors have a very good understanding of the causes of disease and how to protect us.

a What diseases are you protected from? How are you protected?

The cause of disease

In the 1850s many people believed that breathing bad air caused disease. Even scientists at this time thought that microbes just appeared in decayed food. People had no idea of microbes passing from person to person or actually contaminating food.

The first evidence to show that microbes can cause decay and disease was found by a French scientist called Louis Pasteur. He was asked to find out why wine becomes sour. He suspected that microbes were the cause. Pasteur examined soured wine using a microscope and observed yeast cells that are used to make the wine. He also found other microbes that he predicted to cause souring.

To test his prediction, Pasteur heated the wine to 55°C, which is hot enough to kill microbes without spoiling the taste of the wine. This heating process, now called **pasteurisation**, is used to make milk safe to drink.

He showed the importance of his findings when he put 500 litres of wine on board a ship that was going on a 10-month voyage. Half of the wine was pasteurised, and the other half was left untreated. At the end of the voyage the pasteurised wine still had a good flavour but the untreated wine was sour.

Microbes and decay

Pasteur also proved that bacteria do not just appear in decayed food, but that they first contaminate the food and then the food decays. His experiment to prove this is shown here.

KILLER IN THE CLASSROOM

It started when Gareth's mum noticed two tiny spots on her son's hand. The next day, he was dead. Gareth died from a disease called meningitis.

Yesterday Gareth's school was deserted, boycotted by thousands of parents who fear their children are at risk from the invisible killer.

Report adapted from the *Guardian* newspaper, 11.2.99.

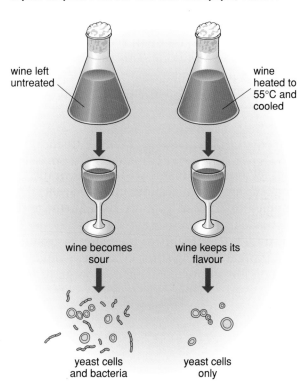

The presence of bacteria makes wine go sour.

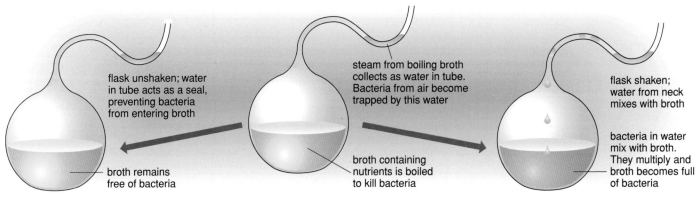

Proving that bacteria cause decay.

b What is the effect of heating and cooling the wine?
Explain why the treatment has this effect.

Spreading disease

Scientists now have a very good understanding of the cause and treatment of disease, and how to prevent it from spreading. Diseases that can spread from person to person are caused by microbes, mainly **bacteria** and **viruses**.

Microbes that cause disease are called **pathogens**. Viral or bacterial pathogens cause many diseases that used to be common in the United Kingdom. The table shows some examples.

Caused by bacterial pathogens	Caused by viral pathogens
Tonsillitis	Common cold
Whooping cough	Influenza (Flu)
Pneumonia	Chicken pox
Tuberculosis (TB)	Measles
Typhoid	AIDS

Smallpox used to be a major killer throughout the world. It has now been eradicated in all countries, saving millions of lives.

Disappearing diseases

Scientists have developed ways of treating disease and even preventing the spread of pathogens. Smallpox used to be one of the world's most deadly diseases. Most people with smallpox died very painfully and those who survived were scarred for life. Smallpox has now been eradicated worldwide and there should never again be an outbreak.

Questions

1 Give two ways in which the virus that causes flu passes from person to person.

2 Use Pasteur's experiments on the causes of decay to answer the following questions.

   a How did Pasteur kill all the microbes in the broth?

   b What prevented microbes from re-entering the flask of broth?

   c What caused the broth to spoil after the microbes had been killed?

   d Explain why the results of this experiment disproved the theory that microbes just appear in decaying food.

Summary

• Pasteur's work showed that living microbes can cause decay and disease.

• Microbes that cause disease are called pathogens.

• Diseases can be caused by both bacterial and viral pathogens.

Feeling ill

Once a viral or bacterial pathogen gets inside your body it starts to reproduce very rapidly. The conditions in your body provide ideal conditions for pathogens to reproduce. You will eventually start to feel ill and feel the **symptoms** of disease.

The symptoms are the effects the disease has on your body. For example, when your body is infected with the flu virus you develop the symptoms of flu – high temperature, headache and aching muscles.

Removing the symptoms

When you have a disease you can be treated with medicines that relieve the symptoms. For example, people with flu take medicines such as **painkillers** to ease the aches and pains. These medicines make them feel better but do not kill the pathogen.

a Give two examples of painkillers people take to ease headaches.

Killing bacteria

Antibiotics are medicines that help to cure diseases caused by bacteria. Antibiotics kill bacteria inside the body. Penicillin was the first antibiotic to be developed, and there are now a large number of different types of antibiotics available.

Antibiotics do not kill viruses. Viruses live and reproduce inside body cells. This makes it difficult to kill them without damaging the cells. Viruses are killed by your body's own defence system. This is explained on pages 8 and 9.

Many diseases make you feel ill by causing pain and a high temperature.

Resistance to antibiotics

Some forms of bacteria have developed resistance to antibiotics, in other words the antibiotic no longer kills the bacteria. **Antibiotic resistance** is the result of using antibiotics too often.

When an antibiotic is used, the non-resistant bacteria in the body are killed but a small number of resistant bacteria remain. These survive and reproduce. Eventually the use of the antibiotic causes the number of resistant bacteria to increase. This is an example of **natural selection**.

To prevent more bacteria becoming resistant, it is important to avoid over-using antibiotics. They should only be used when prescribed by a doctor. A doctor will prescribe an antibiotic when it is needed, such as to treat a kidney infection or pneumonia. Antibiotics may save lives for diseases such as meningitis. By not using antibiotics unnecessarily, you increase the likelihood of them working when you need them.

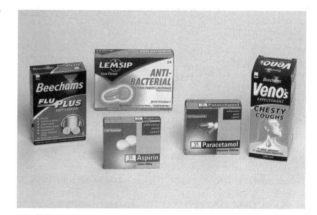

Medicines to relieve pain, lower body temperature and ease sore throats help us to get over common illnesses.

Measuring the effectiveness of antibiotics

The effectiveness of antibiotics can be measured by testing them on bacteria grown in the laboratory. Bacteria can be grown on plates holding a culture medium containing nutrients.

To test antibiotics, small discs of paper containing antibiotic are placed on the culture medium and bacteria are added. The antibiotic diffuses out of the disc and into the culture medium. Bacteria around the disc are killed, leaving a clear zone where they have not grown. The more effective antibiotics leave a wider clear zone.

b Which antibiotic is the most effective in killing bacterial strain Y?

Testing antibiotics

The diagrams show the results of testing different antibiotics on two strains of bacteria. Study them carefully and then answer the questions that follow.

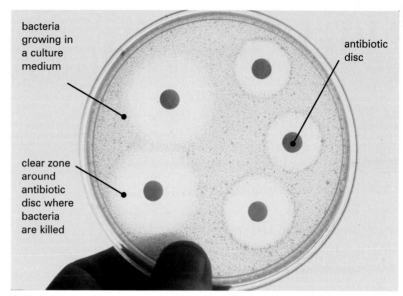

Bacteria growing on a culture medium. The clear zone around the disc is due to bacteria being killed by antibiotic.

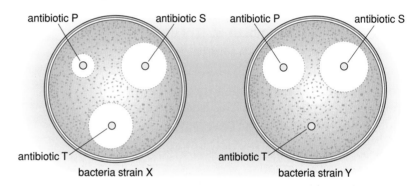

Finding out which antibiotic works best.

Questions

1 a Copy the following table of results. Measure the diameter of the clear zone around each antibiotic disc and complete the table.

	Diameter of clear zone	
	Bacteria strain X	Bacteria strain Y
Antibiotic P		
Antibiotic S		
Antibiotic T		

b Which antibiotic is the most effective in killing both strains of bacteria? Give reasons for your answer.

c Explain why there is no clear zone around the disc with antibiotic T using bacteria strain Y.

2 a Explain the meaning of the term 'antibiotic resistant'.

b Explain why the over-use of antibiotics has caused an increase in the number of strains of antibiotic resistant bacteria.

c What steps need to be taken to stop further strains of resistant bacteria arising?

Summary

- Antibiotics kill bacterial pathogens but cannot be used to kill viral pathogens.

- Many strains of bacteria have developed resistance to antibiotics as a result of natural selection.

- To prevent further resistance arising, it is important to avoid over-use of antibiotics.

20:3 Immunity

Body defences

Your body has several defences to prevent pathogens from infecting it and causing disease:

- ◆ a tough skin covering the surface of your body,

- ◆ blood clots to seal wounds in the skin,

- ◆ sticky mucus and cilia lining your breathing passages,

- ◆ acid produced in your stomach,

- ◆ white blood cells that engulf pathogens at the site of a wound.

You can find out more about each of these defences in the *Humans as Organisms* module.

Even though these defences work very well, some pathogens still manage to get inside your body and start to multiply. This is when your body's **immune system** becomes active.

a **Explain how white blood cells can take in and destroy bacteria.**

Fighting infection

Your body's ability to recognise and destroy pathogens is called an **immune response**. The main type of cell involved is a white blood cell called a **lymphocyte**.

Lymphocytes become active in the presence of a 'foreign' substance called an **antigen**. Most antigens are protein molecules with a particular shape. Antigens are present on the surface of pathogens.

When antigens are detected, lymphocytes produce chemicals called **antibodies**. An antibody is a protein molecule with a specific shape. To destroy a pathogen, an antibody must have just the right shape to attach to the antigens found on the pathogen's surface.

b **Use the diagram on the right to explain why antibodies only destroy specific pathogens.**

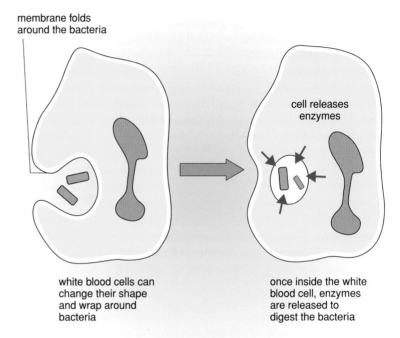

membrane folds around the bacteria

cell releases enzymes

white blood cells can change their shape and wrap around bacteria

once inside the white blood cell, enzymes are released to digest the bacteria

Different types of white blood cell defend your body against disease. This type destroys bacteria by digesting them.

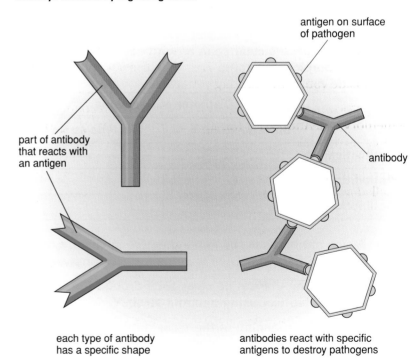

antigen on surface of pathogen

part of antibody that reacts with an antigen

antibody

each type of antibody has a specific shape

antibodies react with specific antigens to destroy pathogens

Antibodies react with specific antigens.

Specialised lymphocytes

Two types of lymphocytes are involved in an immune response. These are **B cells** and **T cells**. They look the same but differ in the way they destroy pathogens.

B cells release antibodies into the blood and are transported to the site of an infection.

T cells have receptors on their surface that can attach to the antigens. T cells then destroy the cells that have the antigen. There are many types of T cell, each with a receptor that can attach to one type of antigen.

T cells also stimulate B cells to multiply and form a clone of identical cells. Some of the cells in the clone are active and release antibodies. Others, called **memory cells**, remain inactive in your body for a very long time after an infection.

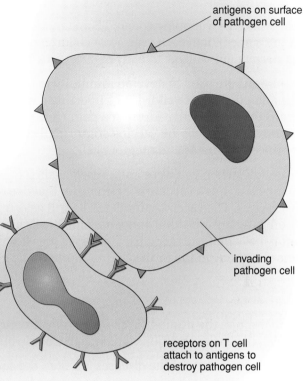

antigens on surface of pathogen cell

invading pathogen cell

receptors on T cell attach to antigens to destroy pathogen cell

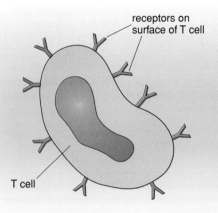

receptors on surface of T cell

T cell

Action of T cells.

Long-term protection

The first time a pathogen enters your body, it takes time for the immune response to destroy it. This gives the pathogen time to breed inside your body, making you feel ill.

If the pathogen enters your body again, it will be recognised by a memory cell. Antibodies will then be produced very rapidly, killing the pathogen before it can breed. This makes you immune to any future infection by the pathogen, because your body can respond rapidly by making the correct antibody. This is called **active immunity**.

Questions

1 Explain why developing immunity to a virus disease does not give you immunity to other diseases caused by viruses.

2 What is meant by the term 'active immunity'?

3 Explain the jobs of the T cells and B cells in producing an immune response.

4 How does your immune system give you long-term protection against disease?

Summary

- Antigens stimulate white blood cells to produce antibodies, which react with and destroy pathogens.

- Two types of lymphocyte cells are involved in the immune response: T cells and B cells.

- T cells have receptors that attach to antigens. They are found on the surface membrane.

- B cells release antibodies into the blood.

- Memory cells remain in the body to give long-term protection against disease.

Developing immunity

Diseases such as whooping cough, TB and measles used to affect thousands of children each year. Most children recover, but some suffer permanent damage to body organs and a few even die.

Vaccinations are used to develop immunity to these diseases. Vaccination involves swallowing or injecting a **vaccine**. This contains dead or inactive forms of a pathogen. Once inside your body, antigens in the vaccine stimulate B cells and T cells to produce antibodies and memory cells.

For example, when you were immunised against measles you were injected with a vaccine containing an inactive form of the measles virus. The vaccine stimulated your B cells to produce antibodies against the viral antigens. Your T cells also produced memory cells that will recognise the active measles virus if it infects your body in the future.

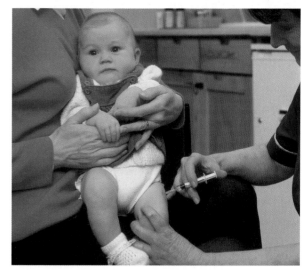

Injecting an inactive form of a pathogen stimulates your body to produce antibodies, giving you protection from the disease.

Saving lives

The table shows the number of cases of three diseases in 1989 and 1999. Each causes serious illness, particularly in children.

The decrease in some of the diseases is due to the success of childhood immunisation programmes. During the 1990s more children were immunised and vaccines became more efficient. Everyone should keep up their immunity. This protects children, their family and the whole community.

The more people that are immunised, the fewer will become infected by diseases. It is hoped that some diseases, such as polio, mumps and measles, will eventually disappear.

Disease	Cases in 1989	Cases in 1999
Whooping cough	10 967	1077
Measles	24 351	2334
Mumps	19 374	1638

Making antibodies

You can develop natural immunity to diseases by becoming infected with the pathogen. Your immunity to more dangerous diseases such as measles is likely to be the result of childhood vaccination. Creating immunity by using vaccines is called **immunisation**. Both are examples of active immunity because your body makes the antibodies that give you immunity.

Injecting antibodies

Developing immunity takes time and sometimes a person needs immediate protection. For example, someone travelling abroad might get bitten by a dog that could be infected with a disease called **rabies**. It is possible to inject the person with antibodies that will destroy the rabies virus. In this case the antibodies are not made by the person's immune system. This is an example of **passive immunity**.

a Explain the differences between 'active' and 'passive' immunity.

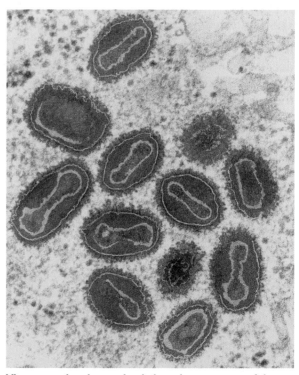

Viruses can be observed only by using very powerful microscopes.

Vaccination programmes

Vaccinations provide protection against several diseases that used to be very common in children. An example is **MMR vaccine** – a combined vaccine to protect against measles, mumps and rubella (German measles). Each of these diseases is caused by a virus that is easily spread from someone with the disease to someone who is not immune.

Vaccines such as MMR have saved millions of children from illness and even death. Before a measles vaccine was available, on average 250 000 children developed measles each year and 85 children died.

The MMR vaccine was introduced in 1988. The large number of babies and children being vaccinated has resulted in a massive decrease in the number of children catching measles.

b What was the maximum number of measles cases between
  i 1960 and 1970?
  ii 1980 and 1990?

Concerns about vaccines

Children who are not vaccinated are much more likely to develop serious illnesses.

In the 1970s parents were concerned about the possible side-effects of the whooping cough vaccine. Fewer children were vaccinated against whooping cough. As a result major outbreaks of this disease occurred, with thousands of children being taken into hospital. When vaccination increased again, there were fewer cases of whooping cough.

Recent concerns about side-effects of the MMR vaccine have led to a decrease in the number of babies receiving the vaccine. In a measles outbreak in London in 2002, 18 out of 20 patients had not received the MMR jab.

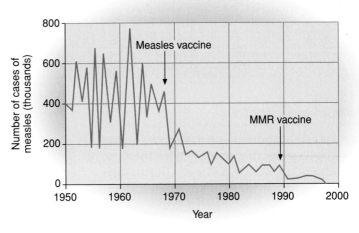

Effect of measles vaccination.

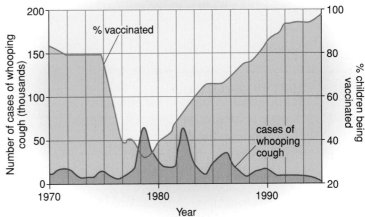

Effect of whooping cough vaccination.

Summary

- People are immunised against a disease by introducing small amounts of dead or inactive forms of the pathogen into the body.

- Vaccination can be used to protect against viral pathogens.

- The MMR vaccine protects children against measles, mumps and rubella.

- Immunity can be active or passive.

- An example of passive immunity is injecting antibodies to protect against rabies.

Questions

1 a How many outbreaks of whooping cough occurred between 1970 and 1990? Give a reason why so many occurred.

  b Explain why the number of whooping cough cases fell in the 1990s.

2 Babies who are breastfed are protected from disease for the first few months of life. This is because of antibodies present in their mother's milk. Is this passive or active immunity? Give reasons for your answer.

Developing immunity

The graph shows what happens when someone is infected by a particular pathogen for the first time. Depending on the pathogen, it can take 3–14 days before antibodies are produced to fight the infection.

The graph also shows what happens when the person is infected again by the same pathogen. Antibodies are produced much more rapidly and in larger amounts. The pathogen is killed very quickly before it can cause illness. This fast response is due to the presence of memory cells that produce the specific antibody needed.

Having memory cells to produce antibodies rapidly explains why you are unlikely to develop any particular infectious disease a second time. For example, once someone has had chicken pox they are then immune to the disease.

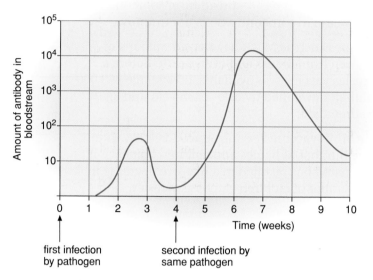

Antibody production after infection.

Wiping out diseases

Many diseases are too serious to risk people becoming infected. For example, polio and smallpox can cause permanent damage and can kill. Vaccines are used to develop immunity to these diseases.

Smallpox is a viral disease which used to kill millions of people. It has now been eradicated across the world following the use of vaccination.

The next disease doctors are aiming to eradicate is polio, which is highly infectious. The virus that causes polio enters the body through the mouth or nose, gets into the blood and is transported around the body. If it reaches the central nervous system it can lead to paralysis – a loss of control of muscles and inability to move.

The graph shows the outbreaks of polio that used to occur in the United Kingdom. Following the use of vaccines, cases of polio no longer occur in this country. The vaccine is very effective and doctors aim to use it to eradicate polio in all countries by 2005.

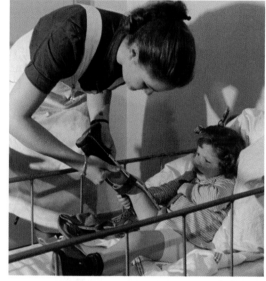

Many children became paralysed as a result of being infected by the polio virus.

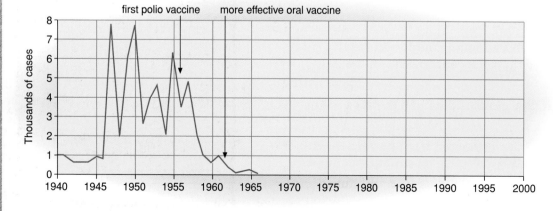

Incidence of paralytic polio in England and Wales since 1940, showing when different vaccines were introduced.

Changing viruses

Influenza or 'flu' is a very common viral disease affecting thousands of people every winter. Symptoms include a sore throat, chesty cough, high temperature, sneezing and a runny nose. Most people quickly recover, but flu can lead to serious problems.

The flu virus is always changing. Next year's virus will be slightly different from this year's, so the immune system will not recognise the virus next time. A new vaccine is produced each year to develop immunity to the changed flu virus. People needing protection need to be treated each year with a new vaccine.

Using the right treatment

When they get flu or a cold, many people expect their doctor to give them an antibiotic. All colds, most coughs and sore throats are caused by viruses, so antibiotics will not help. More bacteria will become resistant to antibiotics if they are used when not needed.

Spreading flu

The map shows the percentage of people infected by flu in a recent outbreak. The flu virus is spread through the air by coughing and sneezing. People become infected by breathing in the virus. Flu spreads more rapidly in more densely populated areas.

Antibiotics are very important medicines but only help to fight infections caused by bacteria.

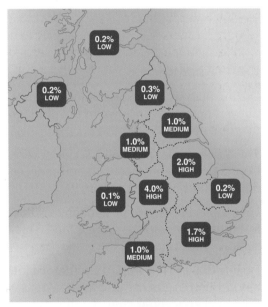

Questions

1 a In the outbreak shown on the map, what was the highest percentage of people with flu?

b In Scotland only 0.2% had flu. The population of Scotland is 5 million. Calculate the number of people in Scotland who suffered from flu.

c 4.0% of people in the West Midlands had flu. Suggest an explanation for the higher rate in that region.

d The symptoms of flu include a sore throat and a headache. Suggest one type of medicine that would be useful in treating these symptoms.

e Why are antibiotics of no use in treating flu?

2 Use the information in the graph showing antibody production to answer the following questions.

a How long did it take to start producing antibodies

  i after the first infection?

  ii after the second infection?

b Explain why antibodies were produced more rapidly after the second infection.

c What was the maximum amount of antibodies in the blood

  i during the first infection?

  ii during the second infection?

d Suggest a reason why more antibodies were produced after the second infection.

Summary

- Some medicines relieve symptoms of disease but do not kill the pathogen.

- To prevent resistance to antibiotics, they must not be over-used.

- Antibiotics do not kill viruses.

- Vaccination can be used to protect against viral pathogens.

20:6 Cleaning the blood

Removing waste

Your kidneys remove **urea**, excess water and excess ions from your blood, to make urine. Urine flows from the kidneys to the bladder, which stores it until it is released when you urinate.

Urea is a toxic substance produced when amino acids are broken down. People whose kidneys do not work properly may die because toxic substances, such as urea, build up in their blood. Their lives can be saved by

- ◆ **transplanting** a healthy kidney from another person, or

- ◆ using a **dialysis** machine to do the job of the kidneys.

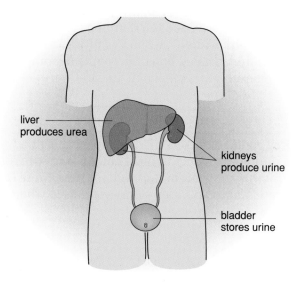

Production of urea and urine.

Kidney dialysis

During dialysis, a person's bloodstream is connected to a dialysis machine as shown in the photograph and in the diagram opposite.

The blood passes through a series of very small tubes made from a partially permeable membrane, each bathed in dialysis fluid.

Urea molecules are small enough to diffuse across the membrane from the blood into the dialysis fluid. This happens because urea is more concentrated in the blood than in the dialysis fluid.

During dialysis it is important that useful substances in the blood, such as glucose and mineral ions, are not lost. To prevent this the dialysis fluid contains the same concentrations of glucose and mineral ions as blood plasma, so only waste substances, excess ions and excess water are removed in the dialysis fluid.

Red and white blood cells are too large to pass through the membrane and so remain in the blood.

At the end of dialysis, the concentration of dissolved substances in the patient's blood is restored to normal levels.

a **As blood flows into the dialysis machine, state one substance which has**
   i **a higher concentration in plasma**
   ii **the same concentration in plasma and dialysis fluid.**

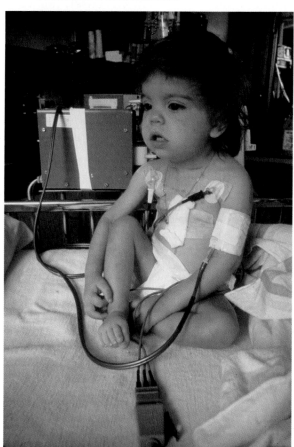

A dialysis machine can be a life saver by removing toxic substances from the blood.

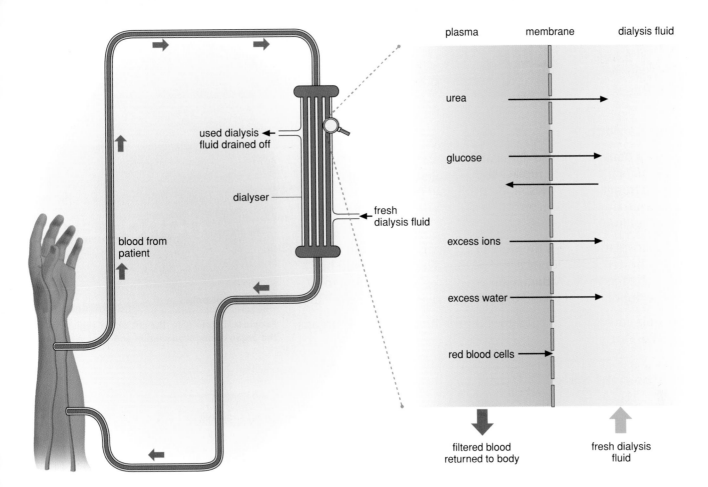

plasma   membrane   dialysis fluid

urea

glucose

excess ions

excess water

red blood cells

filtered blood returned to body

fresh dialysis fluid

During dialysis, waste substances, excess ions and excess water are removed from the patient's blood.

Dialysis fluid contains the same concentrations of glucose and mineral ions as blood plasma.

Regular treatment

Patients need to be connected to a dialysis machine for about 4 hours at a time, and the treatment has to be carried out three times each week. Because of the long time involved in dialysis, patients have to plan their lives around the treatment.

Most patients receiving dialysis treatment look forward to having a transplant. Unfortunately, some people are unsuited for the surgery involved and will need regular dialysis for the rest of their lives.

Questions

1 a Explain why urea diffuses from blood plasma into the dialysis fluid.

 b No glucose is lost during dialysis by having the same concentration of glucose in dialysis fluid as blood plasma. Why is this?

 c Explain why only excess mineral ions and water are removed during dialysis.

 d Why don't red blood cells pass into the dialysis fluid?

2 Suggest why most patients with kidney failure look forward to having a transplant rather than dialysis.

Summary

- People who suffer from kidney failure may be treated by dialysis or by having a kidney transplant.

- By controlling the concentration of substances in dialysis fluid, only waste substances and excess ions and water are removed from the body.

- People receiving dialysis need regular treatment.

Organ transplants

Sometimes a body organ is so damaged by disease that the only way to save the person's life is to replace the damaged organ with a healthy one from another person. Removing an organ, such as a kidney or liver, from one person and putting it into another is called **transplantation**.

A kidney transplant enables the work of a damaged kidney to be carried out by a healthy kidney from a donor. The donor could be someone who has recently died, whose relatives allow doctors to remove the donor's kidneys and use them to save someone else's life.

Many people carry a 'donor card' to show that they want their organs to be used in this way.

People willing to give 'the gift of life' register with the organ donor organisation and carry a donor card.

Getting the right match

A transplanted kidney may be rejected by the immune system, which recognises that the transplant is 'foreign' tissue and tries to reject it from the body. The immune system works in this way to defend the body against organisms such as bacteria that could cause disease.

The following precautions are taken to prevent a transplanted kidney being rejected.

- A donor kidney is used with a 'tissue type' similar to the patient's.
- The patient is kept in sterile conditions for some time after the transplant operation to prevent infection.
- Anti-rejection drugs are used that subdue the cells that produce antibodies.
- The patient's bone marrow may be treated with radiation to stop white blood cells being produced.

After one year 90% of kidney transplants are working, but after 10 years only 50% are still working. Transplanted kidneys fail mainly because of rejection that develops slowly over several years. Some transplants fail because anti-rejection drugs are not taken regularly.

a Which of the following relatives would give the 'best match' for someone needing a kidney transplant: sister, father, or identical twin? Explain your answer.

Many people donate their blood regularly to save lives.

Giving blood

People may lose a lot of blood in an accident or during a major operation such as a kidney transplant. Giving them blood from a blood donor can save their lives. This is called a **blood transfusion.**

It is very important to give the right type of blood. This depends on the person's **blood group**, which is classified as group **A**, **B**, **AB**, or **O**.

The group depends on the antigens present on the surface of red blood cells and the antibodies in blood plasma. The diagram shows the antigens and antibodies in each of the four groups.

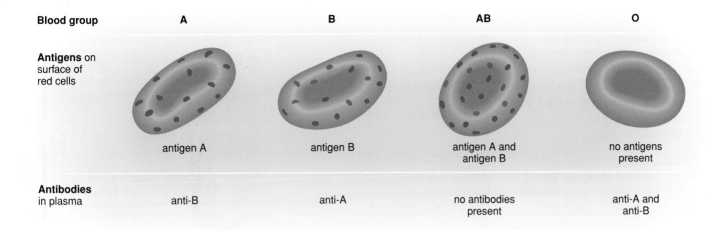

Blood group	A	B	AB	O
Antigens on surface of red cells	antigen A	antigen B	antigen A and antigen B	no antigens present
Antibodies in plasma	anti-B	anti-A	no antibodies present	anti-A and anti-B

Getting the blood group right

If someone is given the wrong type of blood, the red cells in the donated blood will stick together. This is called **agglutination** and can block blood vessels, resulting in organ damage and even death.

For example, agglutination occurs if a recipient with blood group A is given blood from a group B donor, because the anti-B antibodies in the recipient's blood react with antigen B on the donor's red cells. These blood groups are therefore **incompatible**. The table shows which blood groups are compatible.

b What types of antibody are present in the plasma of someone with blood group
  i B?
  ii O?

		Recipient blood group			
		A	B	AB	O
Donor	A	✓	✗	✓	✗
blood	B	✗	✓	✓	✗
group	AB	✗	✗	✓	✗
	O	✓	✓	✓	✓

✓ = recipient accepts transfused blood
✗ = donor's red cells agglutinate

Questions

1 Explain why each of the following procedures is needed for a successful kidney transplant.

  a Matching the tissue type of the donor kidney.

  b Irradiating the patient's bone marrow.

  c Injecting the patient with anti-rejection drugs.

2 Explain why agglutination occurs when group B blood is transfused into the blood of a person with group O.

3 Use the compatibility table to suggest which blood group is called

  a the 'universal donor', and

  b the 'universal recipient'.

  Explain your answer in each case.

4 Describe the advantages and disadvantages of treating kidney failure with a transplant rather than by dialysis.

Summary

• In a kidney transplant, a diseased kidney is replaced with a healthy one.

• Steps are taken to prevent a kidney being rejected by the immune system.

• During a transplant a blood transfusion may be needed.

• This blood must be matched to prevent agglutination.

All the products shown here have one thing in common: we use microorganisms to make them. Microorganisms have been used to make foods and drinks for at least 3000 years. The first was probably wine.

The discovery of wine making was probably accidental, but it was not long before grapes were trodden to press out the juice. This was then left for a few days to turn into wine. Until 150 years ago, no one knew how this worked. People thought that grape juice contained a 'ferment' that made the wine. They did not realise that **fermentation** was carried out by yeast, a microbe. Yeast cells grow naturally on grape skins. When workers trod the grapes, they mixed this yeast with grape juice. A few days later they had wine.

Microbes make all of these for us.

Types of microorganisms

You have already met two types of microorganisms in your *Humans as Organisms* module: bacteria and viruses. Here you will learn about two more – **yeasts** and **moulds**. You can see yeasts as a very fine 'bloom' on unwashed grape skins.

When fruit goes mouldy, the moulds are seen as very fine threads that cause the mouldy area to rot. Like mushrooms, yeasts and moulds are types of **fungi**.

Yeasts

Yeasts are found in dust, soil, water and milk, and even on some of the inside surfaces of our bodies.

Grapes with their own supply of yeast.

Under a microscope they are oval-shaped cells. Mature yeast cells usually have smaller yeast cells attached to them that have been 'budded-off' by asexual reproduction. Under the electron microscope we can see the internal structure of a yeast cell.

a In what ways is a yeast cell
   i   similar to a plant leaf cell?
   ii different from a plant leaf cell?

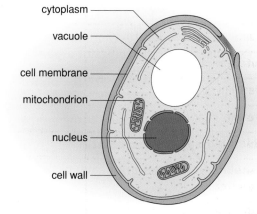

cytoplasm
vacuole
cell membrane
mitochondrion
nucleus
cell wall

Structure of yeast cell.

Moulds

Most moulds live on dead or waste materials and cause these materials to decay. Moulds consist of tiny thread-like structures called **hyphae**. These do not contain separate cells. Each hypha has a cell wall lined with cytoplasm. There are many nuclei in the cytoplasm. Mature hyphae have a central vacuole.

b In what ways is a hypha
   i similar to a plant leaf cell?
   ii different from a plant leaf cell?

Moulds decay materials by feeding on them. Feeding hyphae grow into the material by releasing enzymes that digest the material. The soluble products are then absorbed.

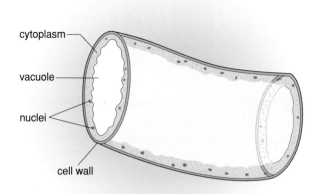

Structure of hypha.

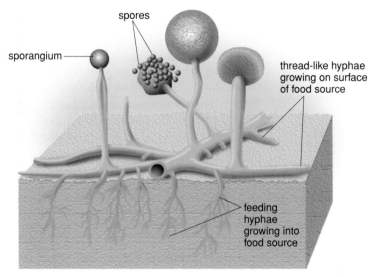

Spores growing.

Moulds reproduce by producing **spores**, each containing a nucleus formed by mitosis. The spores are dispersed by air currents. When a spore lands on food material it germinates to produce hyphae.

c What type of reproduction produces spores?

Question

1 Complete the table with a tick if the structure is present and a cross if not. The first one has been done for you.

Structure	Animal cell	Plant cell	Bacteria	Virus	Yeast	Mould
Nucleus	✓					
Cytoplasm	✓					
Membrane	✓					
Protein coat	✗					
Chloroplast	✗					
Genetic material	✓					
Cell wall	✗					

Summary
- Moulds and yeasts are fungi.
- Yeast cells have a nucleus, cytoplasm and a membrane surrounded by a cell wall.
- Moulds have thread-like structures called hyphae.
- Each hypha has a wall surrounding cytoplasm and many nuclei.
- Moulds reproduce asexually by producing spores.

Microorganisms are very useful in making a large number of foods and drinks. Even some vitamin supplements sold in shops are made from yeast extract.

Feeding microorganisms

If you wanted to grow a microorganism, it would need food. Most microorganisms are similar to animals in that they do not possess chlorophyll, so they cannot produce their own food.

a Name the process that green plants use to make food.

But bacteria and yeasts cannot be fed like animals on solid foods. They have to be provided with food that they can absorb through their cell membranes.

b Some moulds can grow if they are given starch, but they grow much faster if given sugar rather than starch. Explain why.

All the microorganisms used in the home or in industry need carbohydrates such as sugars. Like all other living organisms, microorganisms use carbohydrates as an energy source. They also use them to produce new cells.

c Name the process in all living things that releases energy from sugars.

Like plants, microorganisms such as yeast grow if provided only with sugar and mineral ions. Like plants, yeasts need ions such as nitrate, potassium and phosphate to produce proteins for growth. They also produce their own supply of vitamins.

d What substance can plants, and yeast, produce from nitrates and sugars?

Moulds like those used to produce antibiotics will not grow if given only sugar and ions. These moulds cannot produce their own proteins and vitamins, so these must be supplied.

Microorganisms are usually **cultured** (grown) in a **culture medium** which is either broth or nutrient agar. In industry, they are usually grown in broth. This is like soup – it contains all the nutrients they need.

Nutrient **agar** is often used in laboratories for growing microorganisms. Agar is a jelly-like substance that melts when heated and sets when cooled, but does not contain any nutrients. The nutrients needed by the microorganisms are added and dissolved into molten agar. The nutrient agar sets when poured into a **petri dish** and allowed to cool.

Finally, the microorganisms are inoculated onto the surface of the nutrient agar where they grow to produce colonies that can be seen with the naked eye.

MICROORGANISMS SOLVE FOOD SHORTAGE
There is a serious shortage of meat and other animal protein foods in Russia. To overcome this shortage, microorganisms are grown in industry to produce protein. This is extracted and converted to a powder, which is sprinkled onto vegetable food as a protein supplement.

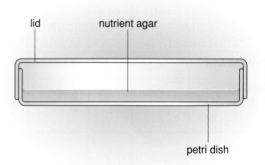

A petri dish for growing microorganisms.

Keeping things sterile

Many different types of microorganisms will grow in nutrient broth or agar. However, most of these do not make useful products, so it is important to prevent cultures of microorganisms from becoming contaminated with unwanted microorganisms. There are two main ways of doing this:

◆ Using sterile equipment and nutrient materials
◆ Preventing contamination from the air.

The diagram shows some of the techniques used in transferring and growing microorganisms.

A FORTUNATE ACCIDENT

A nutrient agar plate being used by Alexander Fleming to grow bacteria became contaminated with a mould called *Penicillium*. Fleming noticed that bacteria around the mould were being killed. Instead of discarding the plate, Fleming investigated why the bacteria were dying. This led to the discovery of antibiotics.

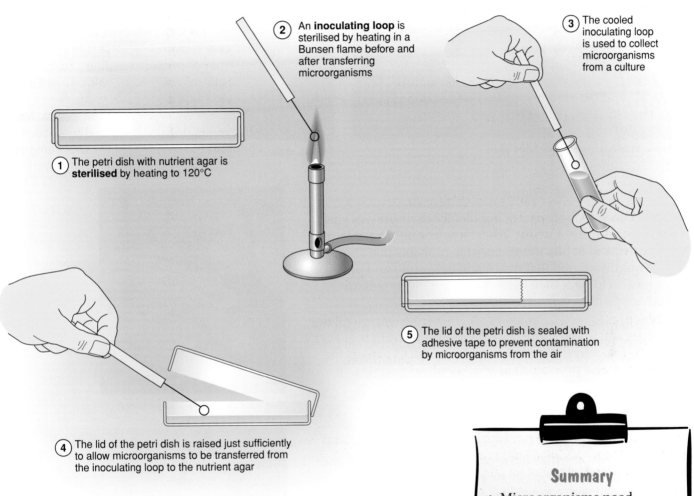

① The petri dish with nutrient agar is **sterilised** by heating to 120°C

② An **inoculating loop** is sterilised by heating in a Bunsen flame before and after transferring microorganisms

③ The cooled inoculating loop is used to collect microorganisms from a culture

④ The lid of the petri dish is raised just sufficiently to allow microorganisms to be transferred from the inoculating loop to the nutrient agar

⑤ The lid of the petri dish is sealed with adhesive tape to prevent contamination by microorganisms from the air

Using sterile techniques to transfer microorganisms.

Danger! Bacteria that cause disease in humans grow best at about 37°C. In school laboratories, bacteria must be grown at a maximum temperature of 25°C. At this temperature useful bacteria grow quickly but harmful bacteria grow slowly.

Questions

1 Why do microorganisms need an energy source?

2 Give two reasons why agar is a useful substance for growing microorganisms.

3 Why is equipment used for growing microorganisms heated to 120°C before use?

Summary

- Microorganisms need carbohydrates as an energy source, and mineral ions to grow. Some also need proteins.

- When growing microorganisms, all equipment and media must be sterilised to prevent contamination.

- Microorganisms from the air must be prevented from entering the medium.

In places, little has changed in 3,000 years.

Getting ready for breakfast.

How bread making began

Bread has been a staple part of our diet for thousands of years. It is made mainly with wheat. Wheat was first cultivated in the Middle East, and at first the grains were probably just chewed. Later it was discovered that they could be ground and made into a paste. This was then hardened over a fire to make a primitive type of bread.

This type of bread is known as unleavened bread. It is much denser than the loaves of today. The texture of unleavened bread is rather like that of a cream cracker biscuit, or pitta bread.

'Get your unleavened bread here!'

Leavened bread

Leavened bread, like our modern loaves, was probably discovered by accident. There are yeast spores everywhere in the air. Some of these may have landed in flour paste that was waiting to be baked. The paste rose before baking, and produced bread with a much lighter texture.

It was then found that keeping a bit of the risen paste back and adding it to the next batch of paste had the same effect. Eventually the Egyptians isolated yeast from the paste and went on to use this yeast to make both bread and beer.

a The quality of the leavened bread produced by the Egyptians was very variable. Suggest a reason for this.

It's warm enough in the sun to make dough rise.

The role of yeast

It was not until the nineteenth century that yeast was shown to be a living organism. Its first scientific name was 'Zuckerpilz' (German for sugar fungus).

b Suggest why it was not until the nineteenth century that yeast was found to be a living organism.

It was Louis Pasteur who investigated how yeast causes **dough** to rise. He showed that yeast respires in the same way as most other living organisms.

$$\text{sugar} + \text{oxygen} \rightarrow \text{carbon dioxide} + \text{water} \; (+ \text{energy})$$

This type of respiration is called aerobic respiration since oxygen is used. The energy released is used in growth and reproduction of yeast cells.

Modern bread making

The diagram shows some of the stages in making bread.

- ◆ The dough containing sugar and yeast is kept warm to allow it to rise.

- ◆ The sugar is used by the yeast in respiration.

- ◆ The yeast releases carbon dioxide.

- ◆ Bubbles of carbon dioxide gas are trapped in the dough, making it rise.

- ◆ When the bread is baked, the high temperature causes the carbon dioxide bubbles to expand, making the bread rise even more.

c **Some bakers add the enzyme amylase to the dough to make the bread rise even further. Explain why this happens.**

Questions

A student investigated the effect of temperature on the rate at which bread dough rises. She placed a 20 mm depth of dough into each of six measuring cylinders. Each cylinder was kept in water at a different temperature. The height of dough in each cylinder was measured after 1 hour. The results are shown in the table.

Temperature of water (°C)	Height of dough (mm)
10	30
20	50
30	95
40	145
50	110
60	40

1 **Plot a graph of the results.**

2 **Calculate the rate at which the dough rose at 30°C.**

3 **Describe and explain the difference between the rates at which the dough rose:**

a **at 10°C and at 20°C**

b **at 40°C and at 50°C**

c **at 50°C and at 60°C.**

4 **Suggest ways in which bakers can avoid contamination of the process by other microorganisms.**

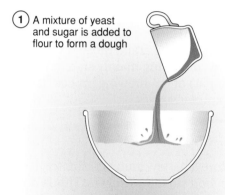
① A mixture of yeast and sugar is added to flour to form a dough

② The dough is kept warm to make it rise

③ The dough continues to rise for part of the baking process

How to make bread.

Summary

- Yeast respires aerobically, oxidising sugar to release carbon dioxide, water and energy.

- In bread making, sugar and yeast are mixed with flour.

- Trapped carbon dioxide bubbles make the dough rise.

Beer is another food product made by using yeast. In this case the source of carbohydrate is barley.

The diagram shows a section through a barley grain. The embryo, which can grow to form stems, roots and leaves, is at one end of the grain. Most of the remainder consists of a food store containing mainly starch. Yeast cannot use starch, so the first part of the brewing process is the breakdown of the starch to simpler sugars.

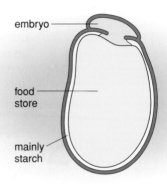

embryo

food store

mainly starch

Cross-section of a barley grain.

Malting

Before a barley grain germinates, it must convert starch from the food store into sugars. This is done by the enzyme amylase which is activated when the seed takes in water. The embryo uses the sugars to provide energy and materials for growth. In a maltings, barley grains are soaked in water to begin this process. After about three days the grain is heated to stop growth, but the temperature used is not high enough to denature the amylase. The barley is now called malt.

Mashing

The malt is crushed, then placed in a mash tun and covered with water at about 65°C. The amylase that was produced during malting now breaks the starch down into sugars. This process takes about an hour. The liquid is now known as wort.

a In what way does this amylase differ from most enzymes that you have studied?

After about an hour the amylase has broken the starch down into sugars that can be used by yeast. The wort is then filtered to remove the barley husks and finally boiled for about another hour.

b Suggest why the wort is boiled.

While the wort is boiling, **hops** are added to it. Substances from the hops give additional flavour to the beer.

Malting barley.

Mashing the malt.

Where the alcohol comes from

The wort is cooled below 20°C, then run into deep fermentation tanks. Now the yeast is added. At first it respires aerobically and multiplies quickly, giving off carbon dioxide gas. The surface of the liquid in the fermentation tank soon becomes covered with a thick foam containing carbon dioxide. This cuts off the oxygen supply to the yeast, which responds by respiring anaerobically.

Anaerobic respiration is respiration without oxygen. You have already met it in muscle in the *Humans as Organisms* module. In yeast, it is similar in one respect – not much energy is released.

Adding the yeast.

But the end products are completely different. In muscle, anaerobic respiration produces **lactic acid**, but in yeast it produces ethanol (alcohol) and carbon dioxide.

The word equation for anaerobic respiration in yeast is

glucose → ethanol + carbon dioxide

After a few days the yeasts respire all the sugar, and fermentation stops. The yeast is then separated from the beer. Some of the beer is used to ferment the next batch of wort. The rest is sold to be used mainly in foodstuffs. The beer is left for a few days to become clear, then it is bottled, canned or stored in barrels.

Wine

Wine is produced when yeast ferments the natural sugars present in grapes. The yeast respires anaerobically just as in beer production.

Modern wine making consists of the following steps.

- ◆ Grapes are crushed mechanically.
- ◆ Grape juice is separated from the skin and stems.
- ◆ Sulphur dioxide is added.
- ◆ Wine yeast is added and fermentation begins.
- ◆ The wine is separated from the yeast, then bottled.

c Explain why malting and mashing are not required in wine making.

Vats for fermenting wine.

Questions

1 List the similarities and differences between aerobic respiration, anaerobic respiration in muscle, and anaerobic respiration in yeast.

2 Three barley grains were given different treatments:

- ◆ Grain A was left dry.
- ◆ Grain B was soaked in boiling water for an hour, then in water at room temperature for 47 hours.
- ◆ Grain C was soaked in water at room temperature for 48 hours.

All three grains were then cut in half and placed, cut surface down, on agar containing starch in a dish as shown in the left diagram.

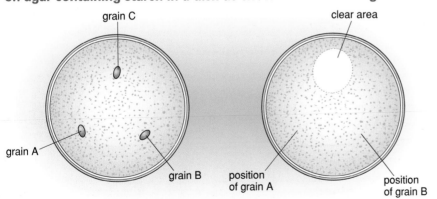

After a further 48 hours the grains were removed and the dish was flooded with iodine solution. The results are shown in the right-hand diagram. Explain the results for

a grain A   **b** grain B   **c** grain C.

Summary

- Both wine and beer are produced by anaerobic respiration in yeast.

- The products of anaerobic respiration are ethanol and carbon dioxide.

- Wine is made from natural sugars in yeast.

- Beer is made from starch in barley grains. Natural enzymes in the grains break the starch down into sugars that yeast can use.

Making cheese

You could probably recite 'Little Miss Muffet' when you were younger, but do you know what 'curds and whey' are? According to legend, cheese was 'discovered' 4000 years ago when an Arab merchant journeyed across the desert, carrying milk in a pouch made from a calf's stomach. Why he thought he could carry milk across a desert for days, we'll never know. The lining of the pouch, combined with the heat of the sun, caused the milk to separate into curds and whey. That night he drank the whey and ate the curds, and thus, so the story goes, cheese was born.

When milk goes sour it curdles. The milk proteins separate out as solid **curds**. The liquid is now clear and is called **whey**. The curds can be dried and eaten straight away as 'cottage cheese'. The whey can be fed to animals. If water is pressed out of the curds and they are then left to mature, a solid cheese is produced.

The ancient Greeks and Romans realised that they did not have to wait for milk to go sour to make cheese. They speeded up the process by adding sour milk to fresh milk.

We now know how this works. Milk goes sour when lactic acid bacteria called *Lactobacillus* ferment the milk sugar (**lactose**) to form lactic acid. These bacteria are present on the skin of cows, which is how they easily get into milk.

lactose + water → lactic acid

The lactic acid produced by the bacteria lowers the pH of the milk sufficiently to make the protein coagulate.

In modern cheese production, the milk is first pasteurised by heating it to 135°C for one second, then cooling it rapidly. A culture of *Lactobacillus lactis* is then added to produce the curds.

a Suggest why milk is pasteurised before being used in cheese making.

The curds are then matured to form cheese. Different cheeses are made by the action of different microorganisms during the maturing process. Hard cheeses like Cheddar are ripened by lactic acid bacteria. Soft cheeses like Camembert are ripened by enzymes from yeasts that grow on the surface. Introducing *Penicillium* mould with needles ripens blue-veined cheeses.

Separating curds from whey in a cheese factory.

RENNET OR ENZYME?

The curdling process in cheese used to be speeded up by using dried rennet from calves' stomachs. Now, scientists have genetically engineered an enzyme, chymosin, which works in the same way. So calves are no longer killed for their stomach lining. Genetic engineering is not all bad!

Different microorganisms give the distinct flavour to each kind of cheese.

Making yoghurt

Yoghurt is the Turkish word for sour milk. It used to be made by adding yoghurt to fresh milk, but yoghurt factories now use pure cultures of bacteria to ensure that the yoghurt always tastes the same.

In yoghurt making, all the milk goes solid rather than becoming separated into curds and whey, so different bacteria are used. The milk used is also different. It is usually homogenised and sterilised, with added milk proteins.

After sterilising and cooling to 45°C, a starter culture of bacteria is added. The most common are *Streptococcus thermophilus* and *Lactobacillus vulgaris*. Both are needed and both produce lactic acid. *Streptococcus* works first, lowering the pH of the milk to 5.0. Then *Lactobacillus* lowers it further to about 4.0. The change in pH coagulates the milk proteins and the whole of the milk goes solid. This process takes about 5 hours.

When the pH reaches 4.0, the yoghurt is cooled quickly. It is then put into pots and sealed.

Yoghurt has a shelf life of about 2–3 weeks if refrigerated. After that it begins to taste sour.

b Explain why the yoghurt is rapidly cooled when the pH reaches 4.0.

c Why does yoghurt go sour after 2–3 weeks in a fridge? (In your exam you will not need to remember the names of the bacteria used in these processes.)

How are different yoghurts made?

◆ *Natural yoghurt* has nothing else added – no stabilisers, no sweeteners, etc. It is a good alternative to custard and ice cream for fruit crumbles and great with cereals.

◆ *Smooth* and *creamy* has added sugar, fruits, etc. – even a layer of cream on top.

◆ *Greek-style yoghurts* are strained, which is why they are thicker, but they are also made with whole milk or ewe's milk, which is higher in fat anyway.

◆ *Low-fat yoghurts* are made with semi-skimmed or skimmed milk, sometimes with added skimmed milk powder to make them taste smoother. They have few calories but taste more sour.

Questions

1 What type of reaction is the production of lactic acid?

2 Why does milk go solid in cheese and yoghurt making?

3 Why is it important

  a to heat milk before using it to make yoghurt and cheese?

  b to use starter cultures of bacteria rather than old yoghurt to begin the reaction?

4 List the similarities and differences between cheese and yoghurt production.

All yoghurts are made by bacteria.

Summary

- Cheese and yoghurt are made by using bacteria that ferment lactose to lactic acid.

- Lactic acid lowers the pH of milk, causing the protein in milk to coagulate.

- In cheese making, the solid curds are removed from the liquid whey, then dried and matured.

- In yoghurt making, lactic acid makes the whole of the milk go solid.

Microorganisms are also used to make drugs. These have extremely complicated molecules and are produced only in tiny amounts by microorganisms.

To make large quantities of drugs, microorganisms have to be grown in very tightly controlled conditions. They are grown in **fermenters** like the one shown in the diagram.

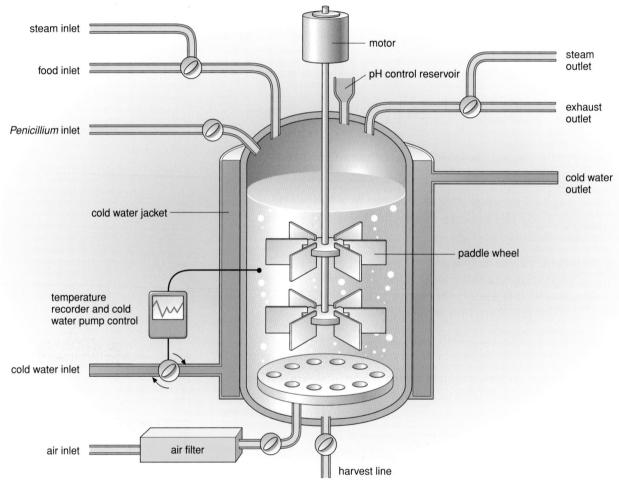

A fermenter for producing antibiotics.

The mould *Penicillium* makes the antibiotic **penicillin**. The mould is provided with the conditions needed for optimum growth in the fermenter. This can have a capacity as large as 150 000 litres. The food material is usually a substance called corn-steep liquor. This is a waste product that contains sugar and other nutrients needed by the *Penicillium*.

All the processes you have studied so far in this unit have been anaerobic. *Penicillium* needs plenty of oxygen to grow quickly. Air is pumped in through the base of the fermenter and distributed by holes that produce air bubbles. The bubbles also help to mix the contents of the fermenter.

a The air is filtered before entering the fermenter. Suggest why.

NATURAL ANTIBIOTICS
Moulds like *Penicillium* produce antibiotics in the wild to kill competitors. In the wild they live on dead matter. Spores land on this and produce digestive hyphae. These secrete antibiotics to kill any other microorganisms that might be feeding on the material. We now grow these moulds to produce antibiotics that we use to kill disease-causing microorganisms.

When the fermenter is set up, steam is blown through the contents to raise the temperature to 24°C – the optimum temperature. The steam supply is then turned off. After a while, cold water has to be pumped around the cooling jacket to prevent the temperature rising higher than 24°C.

b Explain why the temperature inside the fermenter begins to rise above 24°C.

The contents of the fermenter are stirred by a rotating paddle wheel. This helps to keep the temperature even throughout the fermenter, and prevents the mould from settling at the bottom. The pH of the contents is adjusted to about 7.4 for optimum growth.

c Explain why growth would not be as rapid if the mould sank to the bottom of the fermenter.

d What would be added to the contents of the fermenter if the pH rose above the optimum value?

Fermentation takes about a week altogether, but penicillin is not produced until most of the nutrients have been used up for growth.

Industrial fermenters in a penicillin factory.

Questions

1 Describe the factors needed for maximum rate of production of penicillin in a fermenter.

2

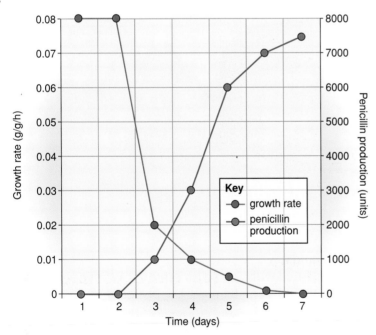

The graph shows how the rate of penicillin production is related to the rate of growth of the mould.

a Describe how mould growth rate varies with time.

b Describe how penicillin production varies with time.

c Suggest an explanation for the relationship between these two rates.

Summary
- Fermenters have
  - an air supply to provide oxygen for respiration
  - a stirrer to keep the contents mixed and at an even temperature
  - a water-cooled jacket to remove the heat released by respiration
  - instruments to monitor temperature and pH.
- Penicillin is made by growing *Penicillium* in a fermenter. The mould produces penicillin when it has used up most of the nutrients.

Energy for developing countries

Most developing countries are short of fuel for cooking. Often, no fossil fuels are available and wood is scarce. There is little money to import fuels. An alternative, cheap fuel that is readily available is the dung produced every day by farm animals. These can be dried and burnt directly as fuel, or fermented by bacteria to produce '**biogas**' for cooking and heating.

Anaerobic bacteria that ferment materials in faeces produce biogas. The residual material is known as effluent. Biogas consists mainly of methane – a hydrocarbon gas. The effluent is very rich in nutrients thanks to the action of the bacteria. The diagram shows a biogas generator suitable for providing biogas for a small Third World farm.

Dung – the developing world's sustainable fuel.

Wood fires destroy trees and cause pollution.

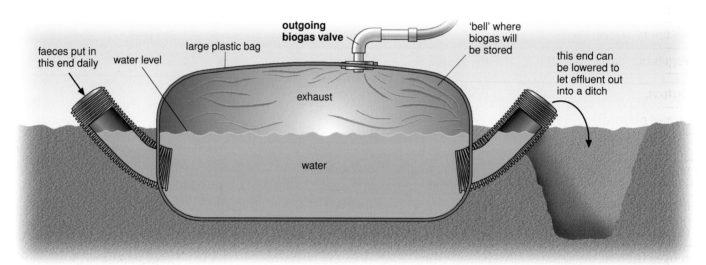

Developing-world gas production.

A trench about 10 m long and 1 m deep is dug in the ground, and a heavy-duty plastic bag is then placed in the trench. The bag is fitted with inlet and outlet pipes and a valve to draw off the gas. To start up the digester, the bag is two-thirds filled with water, then topped off with the exhaust gases from a car. Then a mixture of water and dung is fed through the inlet pipe. It takes about 18 kg of faeces per day to provide enough gas for the farmer's needs. The methane produced is released through the valve at the top. Effluent to fertilise the crops can be run off by lowering the outlet pipe into the ditch.

a **i** Name the main gas in the car exhaust fumes.
    ii Why is the plastic tube topped up with this gas?

b List the factors that influence the rate at which biogas is produced in this setup. Explain how each factor will have its effect.

Making better use of domestic waste

We can generate biogas on a large scale from manure and organic waste. The diagram shows a scheme that operates in Kristianstad in Sweden. The biogas is produced in the digester. Most of the gas is piped to a district-heating supply in the town.

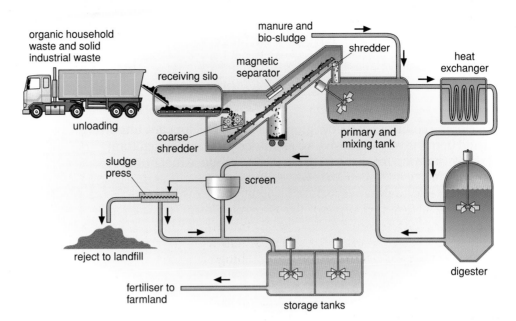

Producing gas from city refuse. The gas is drawn from both the primary/mixing tank and the digester.

The table shows this plant's inputs, outputs and energy statistics.

Input	Tonnes
Manure	41 200
Household waste	3 100
Abattoir waste	24 600
Distillery waste	900
Vegetable waste	1 400

Output	Tonnes
Liquid biofertiliser	67 150
Biogas	4 000
Waste	50

Energy statistics	MWh
Gross biogas production	20 000
Biogas used to heat plant	2 100
Biogas sales to district heating plan	17 900
Electricity purchased to operate biogas plant	540

Questions

1 For the Swedish biogas digester, calculate

   a the percentage mass of the input material that is converted into biogas

   b the percentage of the output that is waste.

2 Calculate the proportion of the biogas output that is needed to heat and operate the plant.

3 List the advantages and disadvantages of producing fuel in this way rather than using North Sea gas.

Summary

• Biogas is mainly methane.

• It is produced by anaerobic fermentation of organic waste.

• Many different organisms, including anaerobic bacteria, are involved in anaerobic breakdown.

• Biogas is used as a fuel both in the home and in industry.

Developing countries can now 'grow' their own fuel for cars. Importing oil and petrol is very expensive for countries with only agricultural produce to export, so many have decided to produce fuel from crops.

Sugar cane crop being harvested.

Car filling with gasohol in Brazil.

Brazil has done this most successfully by growing sugar cane to produce ethanol. This is mixed with petrol to make a fuel called **gasohol**. Car engines have been adapted to run on gasohol or on pure ethanol – though a little petrol is added to the ethanol to stop people from drinking it!

Sugar cane grows quickly in tropical climates, producing two crops per year. The cane is taken to mills and crushed by enormous rollers to extract the juices. These are then refined to produce the 'cane sugar' that we put in tea and coffee. There are two waste products – bagasse and molasses. Bagasse is the fibrous remains of the plants after crushing. Molasses is a syrupy liquid left after cane sugar has been extracted from the juices. These waste products can be used to make ethanol.

Rollers crushing sugar cane in mill.

Making ethanol from sugar cane

Molasses contains lots of sugars. Adding yeast to molasses has the same effect as adding it to wort in brewing. The yeast respires anaerobically, producing ethanol and carbon dioxide. The fully fermented liquid contains about 10% ethanol. Water is then removed from it by fractional distillation. When the liquid is heated, alcohol evaporates first because it has a lower boiling point than water. The vapour is cooled to condense the ethanol.

The thermal energy for distillation is provided by burning the bagasse. The purified ethanol is either used as a fuel by itself or mixed with petrol. In Brazil gasohol contains 22% ethanol, but in most other countries no more than 10% ethanol is added.

Industrial ethanol distillation columns.

In the USA ethanol is produced from maize rather than sugar. Maize is a cereal crop, like barley, so it stores carbohydrates as starch rather than sugar.

a What additional process is required to produce ethanol from maize rather than sugar cane?

Pros and cons

Producing ethanol for use as a fuel is beneficial because, unlike oil, the source is renewable. There are several other advantages. Burning fossil fuels releases carbon dioxide into the atmosphere. So does burning ethanol – but this is only replacing the carbon dioxide that the sugar plants took in during photosynthesis.

b What is expected to happen if the carbon dioxide content of the atmosphere continues to rise?

Burning ethanol also produces less air pollution than burning oil. The table shows the changes in pollutant levels in Brazil since the introduction of gasohol. The data show average emissions per car or van of CO (carbon monoxide), HC (hydrocarbons) and NO_x (nitrous oxides) in grams per kilometre travelled.

Year	Fuel	Pollutant (g/km)		
		CO	HC	NO_x
<1980	Petrol	54.0	4.7	1.2
1986	Gasohol	22.0	2.0	1.9
	Ethanol	16.0	1.6	1.8
1990	Gasohol	13.3	1.4	1.4
	Ethanol	10.0	1.3	1.2
1995	Gasohol	4.7	0.6	0.6
	Ethanol	3.2	0.4	0.3

c i Describe the trends in the data.
ii Explain the effect these changes will have on the environment in Brazil.

There are some problems in replacing oil with ethanol. Many people are concerned that rainforests are being cleared to provide sugar cane plantations, and that small farmers are being displaced. Others argue that the ethanol would be used more effectively in the chemical industry to make plastics.

Question

1 The US government is encouraging the use of ethanol-based fuels. The extract is from a group opposed to this. Use the information in the passage and the rest of this spread to evaluate the case for using ethanol-based fuels in the USA.

An acre of US maize yields about 328 gallons of ethanol. But planting 1 acre of maize requires about 140 gallons of fossil fuel. Thus, even before maize is converted to ethanol, the feedstock costs $1.05 per gallon of ethanol. About 70% more energy is required to produce ethanol than the energy that is actually in ethanol. Every time you make 1 gallon of ethanol, there is a net energy loss of 54,000 BTU. Ethanol from maize costs about $1.74 per gallon to produce, compared to about 95 cents to produce a gallon of petrol. The average US car travelling 10,000 miles a year on pure ethanol (not a petrol–ethanol mix) would need about 852 gallons of the maize-based fuel. This would take 11 acres to grow, based on net ethanol production. This is the same amount of cropland required to feed seven Americans. If all the cars in the United States were fuelled with 100% ethanol, a total of about 97% of US land area would be needed to grow the maize feedstock. Maize would cover nearly the total land area of the United States.

Summary
- Ethanol-based fuels can be produced by the anaerobic fermentation of sugar cane juice or from glucose from maize starch.
- The ethanol is distilled from the products of fermentation.

1 Copy and use words from the list to complete the sentences below.

antibiotics antibodies antigens

lymphocytes painkillers vaccines

Bacteria infecting the body are killed using _____ . Other medicines, such as _____, are used to ease some of the symptoms of the infection. Cells in the body called _____ produce _____ to destroy the bacteria.

2

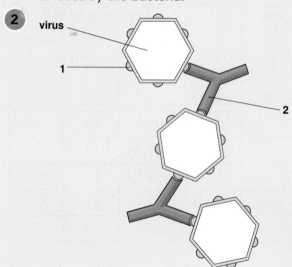

virus

1

2

a i Name the structure labelled 1.

ii Name the structure labelled 2.

b Use the diagram to explain why antibodies only destroy particular types of pathogen.

3 a Copy and complete the table below.

Blood group	Antigens present	Antibodies present
A	A	
B		Anti A
	A and B	none
O	none	

b i Where are the blood group antigens found?

ii Where are the blood group antibodies found?

c Explain what happens if blood containing antigen A is mixed with blood containing anti-A antibodies.

4 The graph shows the number of cases of polio in England and Wales from 1940 to 1975.

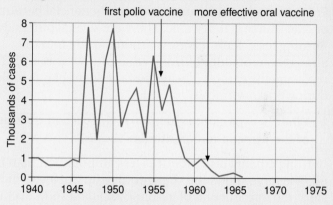

first polio vaccine   more effective oral vaccine

Thousands of cases

a What was the highest number of cases of polio recorded?

b When was the polio vaccine first used?

c Describe the evidence which shows that the second vaccine is more effective.

d Explain as fully as you can why vaccination develops immunity to polio.

e Developing immunity using vaccination is an example of active immunity. Explain the meaning of the term 'active immunity'.

5 The diagram shows the results of an investigation to measure the effect of different antibiotics on a bacterium that causes throat infections. Each disc contains the same concentration of antibiotic.

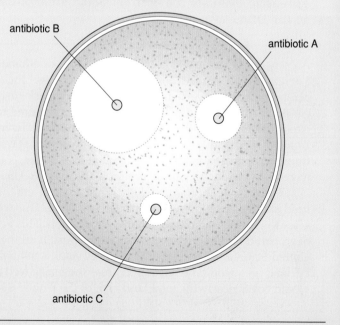

antibiotic B

antibiotic A

antibiotic C

a Explain why there is a clear zone around each disc.

b Which of the following is the most accurate conclusion for the investigation? Explain your answer.

   1 Antibiotic B kills more bacteria than A and C.

   2 Antibiotic C kills the least number of bacteria.

   3 Antibiotic B is twice as effective as A and three times as effective as C.

c Antibiotic C was used frequently over many years to treat throat infections. Doctors have recently found that antibiotic C is now much less effective. Suggest why.

6 All medicines can have side effects and vaccines are among the safest medicines in use. Recent concerns about side effects of the MMR vaccine have led to a decrease in the number of babies being vaccinated. The table shows some of the problems linked with the MMR vaccine compared with the natural diseases (measles, mumps and rubella).

Condition	Chance after disease	Chance after MMR vaccine
Convulsions (fits)	1 in 200	1 in 1000
Blood clotting problems	1 in 3000	1 in 24 000
Death	1 in 2500-5000 depending on age	0

a Why does the MMR vaccine give immunity to three different diseases?

b Use the evidence in the table to present three reasons to support the use of MMR vaccine.

7 a i Describe the malting stage in the production of beer.

   ii Explain why the malting stage is necessary.

b In an investigation, equal volumes of standard yeast suspension were mixed with solutions of the sugars glucose, maltose and lactose. The sugar solutions were of equal concentration and volume. The volume of carbon dioxide (CO_2) given off by each mixture is shown in the table.

Mixture	Volume of CO_2 produced after				
	15 min	30 min	45 min	60 min	75 min
Yeast + glucose	1	10	18	45	90
Yeast + maltose	0	1	3	6	10
Yeast + lactose	0	0	0	0	0

   i Describe how the production of carbon dioxide by the yeast–glucose mixture varied with time.

   ii Suggest an explanation for differences between the rate of production of carbon dioxide by the yeast–glucose mixture and (1) the yeast–maltose mixture; (2) the yeast–lactose mixture.

8 a Give two advantages of using ethanol-based fuels rather than fossil fuels.

b The graph shows how the concentrations of sugar and ethanol varied with time in an industrial process.

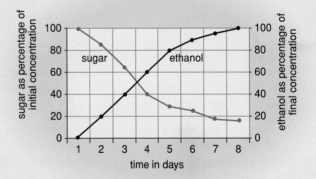

   i Describe how the concentration of ethanol in the process varied with time.

   ii Use information from the graph to suggest an explanation for the shape of the curve for ethanol.

c What further stages are needed following fermentation to produce ethanol-based fuels?

9 Describe how bacteria from a pot of yoghurt could be transferred to sterile agar in a petri dish. Explain the reason for each procedure.

Extended homework questions

1 The bar chart shows the percentage of bacteria that are resistant to antibiotics. The data were obtained from samples of bacteria from hospital patients in England and Wales.

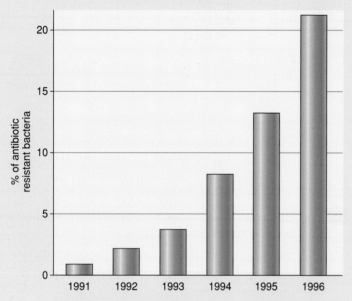

a What is meant by 'antibiotic resistance'?
b Calculate the percentage increase in antibiotic resistance between
  i 1994 and 1995
  ii 1995 and 1996.
c Explain why the percentage of antibiotic-resistant bacteria increased during this time.
d Suggest why increasing antibiotic resistance causes problems in treating patients.

2 Whooping cough is a highly infectious disease caused by a bacterium. The graph shows how cases of whooping cough were affected by the introduction of antibiotics and vaccines.

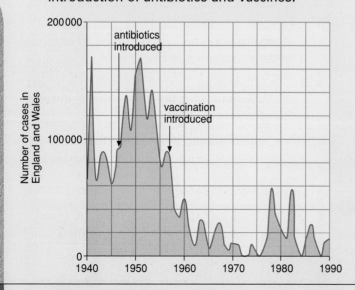

a When were
  i antibiotics
  ii vaccines
  first used to treat whooping cough?
b Describe how the cases of whooping cough changed after introducing
  i antibiotics
  ii vaccines.
c Explain why antibiotics help someone recover from whooping cough.
d Why did the number of cases of whooping cough decrease after the introduction of vaccination?
e In the 1970s and 1980s parents became concerned about possible side-effects of the whooping cough vaccine and many did not get their children vaccinated. Describe the likely effect of having fewer children vaccinated.

3 The ABO system of blood groups is based on antigens and antibodies found in the blood.

a Where in the blood are the antigens found?
b Where in the blood are the antibodies found?

The table shows the compatibility of blood groups for transfusion.

		Recipient blood group			
		A	B	AB	O
Donor	A	✓	✗	✓	✗
blood	B	✗	✓	✓	✗
group	AB	✗	✗	✓	✗
	O	✓	✓	✓	✓

✓ = recipient accepts transfused blood
✗ = donor's red cells agglutinate

c Explain the meaning of 'agglutination'.
d Which blood groups can a patient with group A be given during transfusion?
e Explain why a group B patient cannot receive blood from a group A donor.
f Use the data in the table to explain why blood group O is described as the 'universal donor'.

Sulphuric acid and development

Because sulphuric acid has so many important industrial uses, its production can be used to show how industrially developed a country or region is. The more industrially developed a country, the more sulphuric acid it has to produce. Look at the graphs and answer these questions.

1 Which of the regions shown is the most industrially developed, and which is the least?

2 By approximately how many years does the development of the USSR appear to lag behind that of the USA ?

3 The USSR and Japan show similar trends up to 1960. Describe how their industrial development changed from then on.

4 In approximately which year did the East Asian region overtake Japan in terms of industrial development?

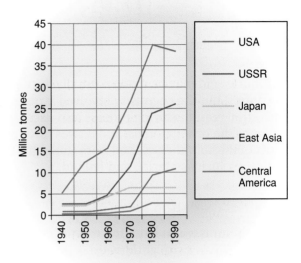

Regional production of sulphuric acid.

Sulphuric acid and fertilisers

You know that fertilisers need to contain nitrogen, but the element phosphorus is important too. The most common source material for this is calcium phosphate, which occurs naturally in rocks.

Unfortunately calcium phosphate is insoluble in water, so it has to be converted into a soluble compound so that plants can absorb it easily. The most useful compound is ammonium phosphate, $(NH_4)_3PO_4$. This is made by reacting ammonia (NH_3) directly with phosphoric acid solution (H_3PO_4).

d Write a balanced chemical equation for this reaction.

e Why is ammonium phosphate a good fertiliser in addition to containing phosphorus?

The phosphoric acid needed for this reaction is made by heating calcium phosphate with sulphuric acid. This is such an important usage that many fertiliser plants manufacture their own sulphuric acid on site.

$$\text{calcium phosphate} + \text{sulphuric acid} \rightarrow \text{calcium sulphate} + \text{phosphoric acid}$$

Questions

1 Balance the chemical equation for phosphoric acid production:

$$Ca_3(PO_4)_2 \text{ (s)} + 3H_2SO_4 \text{ (aq)} \rightarrow CaSO_4 + H_3PO_4$$

2 Explain why pollution prevention in factories can never entirely remove the problem of acid rain from the Earth.

Summary
- Sulphuric acid is made from sulphur, oxygen (from air) and water.
- It is a very important industrial chemical.
- The manufacture of sulphuric acid is sometimes used as a measure of the industrial development of a country.

Sulphuric acid may be made naturally during volcanic eruptions, but the chemistry involved is quite complex. The industrial manufacturing process also uses sulphur, air and water as the raw materials, and passes through several stages. Most of the sulphur is mined from underground deposits in countries such as Mexico and Poland.

1 Initial oxidation

The sulphur is burnt in air to form the choking gas sulphur dioxide. This is a straightforward oxidation reaction.

sulphur + oxygen → sulphur dioxide

a **Write a balanced chemical equation for this reaction.**

b **What does the colour of the damp pH paper tell you about this gas?**

c **The gas produced by this reaction is passed through a heat exchanger to make steam. Why is it so hot?**

Sulphur burns in air to produce poisonous sulphur dioxide gas.

2 Secondary oxidation

The sulphur dioxide is sprayed with water to wash out any dust or other impurities. It is then dried before it is pumped into a heated chamber with more air. Here the gases pass over a vanadium oxide (V_2O_5) catalyst, where a secondary oxidation takes place, turning the sulphur dioxide into sulphur trioxide.

$$\text{sulphur dioxide} + \text{oxygen} \rightarrow \text{sulphur trioxide}$$
$$2SO_2 + O_2 \rightarrow 2SO_3$$

d **Which metal family do you think vanadium is in? Explain your answer.**

3 Reaction with water

In theory, sulphuric acid may then be made by dissolving the sulphur trioxide in water.

sulphur trioxide + water → sulphuric acid

e **Write a balanced chemical equation for this reaction.**

f **Draw your own annotated flow diagram for the production of sulphuric acid, describing what happens at each stage.**

In practice, this reaction is so strongly exothermic that a dangerous acid mist is formed, which is difficult to contain. Instead, the sulphur trioxide is dissolved in concentrated sulphuric acid to form **fuming sulphuric acid** (*oleum*). This is then slowly and carefully diluted with water to give concentrated sulphuric acid once again (98% H_2SO_4).

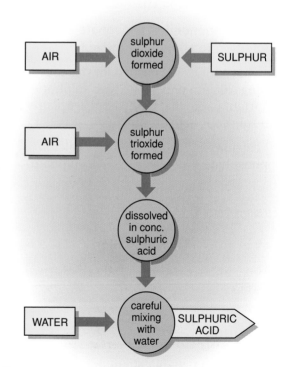

Flow chart for the industrial manufacture of sulphuric acid.

More about stage 2 – the contact process

The heart of this process is the oxidation of sulphur dioxide to sulphur trioxide. This happens when the sulphur dioxide and oxygen come into contact on the surface of the vanadium oxide catalyst. Therefore, this method of making sulphuric acid is often called the **contact process**.

The use of a catalyst here is essential as the reaction is reversible:

$$2SO_2 + O_2 \xrightleftharpoons[\text{endothermic back reaction}]{\text{exothermic forward reaction}} 2SO_3$$

As the forward reaction is exothermic, the best yields are obtained at low temperatures, but the reaction is far too slow then to be of any use industrially.

An obvious way to speed the reaction up would be to raise the temperature, but the yield falls rapidly above 450°C, dropping to zero by 1000°C. Unfortunately the reaction is still too slow at 450°C. The temperature would need to be raised to 800°C or more to make the reaction go fast enough.

g Why is this reaction not run at 800°C?

This is where the vanadium oxide comes in. This catalyst lets the reaction run fast enough at 450°C, giving a yield of 98% sulphur trioxide.

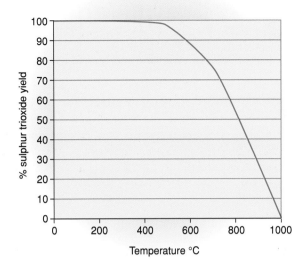

Effect of temperature on sulphur trioxide yield.

Questions

Look at the equation for sulphur trioxide production.

1 How many particles are there on each side of the equation?

2 How many dm³ of sulphur trioxide could be made from 2 dm³ of sulphur dioxide and 1 dm³ of oxygen (at the same temperature and pressure)?

3 What effect would increasing the pressure have on the yield from this reaction? Explain your answer.

4 This reaction could be run at high pressure and high temperature without a catalyst. Why do you think a catalyst is used instead of high pressure?

Summary

- Sulphuric acid is made from sulphur, air and water.

- Sulphur is burnt in air to form sulphur dioxide.

- The sulphur dioxide is further oxidised to sulphur trioxide using a vanadium oxide catalyst.

- The sulphur trioxide is dissolved in concentrated sulphuric acid which is then carefully diluted with water.

- The oxidation of sulphur dioxide is a reversible reaction.

Sulphuric acid as a drying agent

The test for water.

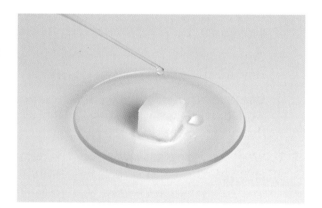

The test for concentrated sulphuric acid.

Before sulphur dioxide is oxidised to sulphur trioxide it is washed and dried. What might surprise you is that the gas is dried using concentrated sulphuric acid.

Concentrated sulphuric acid has a strong affinity for water. It can extract the water of crystallisation from compounds such as copper sulphate. The familiar blue crystals of copper sulphate crumble to a white powder if concentrated sulphuric acid is poured over them. This is the reverse of the test for water.

a **Blue anhydrous cobalt chloride turns pink when water is added. What would happen if concentrated sulphuric acid were added to pink hydrated cobalt chloride?**

Dehydration

Dehydration means the removal of water. Concentrated sulphuric acid is such a good dehydrating agent that it can even pull the elements of water out of some organic compounds!

If you drop concentrated sulphuric acid onto a sugar cube, for example, a violent reaction takes place and all that is left behind is a black mass of carbon.

$$\text{sugar (sucrose)} \xrightarrow{\text{concentrated sulphuric acid}} \text{carbon} + \text{water}$$
$$C_{12}H_{22}O_{11} \xrightarrow{\hspace{3cm}} 12C + 11H_2O$$

b **Write a balanced chemical equation for the dehydration of glucose ($C_6H_{12}O_6$).**

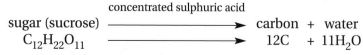

Extracting the 'water' from sugar.

Sulfacom product information

Product name:	**Concentrated sulphuric acid**
Old name:	Oil of vitriol
Molecular formula:	H_2SO_4
Purity:	98%
Melting point:	10.3°C
Boiling point:	338°C
Density:	1.94 g/cm³
Appearance:	Colourless oily liquid
Stability:	Stable; but avoid water, most common metals, organic materials, etc.
Safety:	Extremely corrosive; causes serious burns; highly toxic; harmful by ingestion and inhalation – may cause permanent lung damage in extreme cases

1 Spare bottles of concentrated sulphuric acid are sometimes kept in outdoor storage bins for safety. What problem might this cause if laboratory supplies had to be quickly replenished on a frosty day?

2 Safety glasses and rubber gloves are recommended when handling acid. Why?

3 If an acid bottle broke in a metal workshop, what additional hazard might be present, alongside the obvious ones of broken glass and corrosive acid?

4 Concentrated sulphuric acid reacts violently with water in a strongly exothermic reaction. If a small amount of water is added to the acid, it starts to boil and produce a fine acid mist. Why is this mist so dangerous?

5 The 2-litre glass acid bottles weigh 300 g when empty. How much do they weigh when full?

6 Calculate the formula mass of sulphuric acid. Use this to work out the mass of sulphur needed to make 1 tonne of this product.

7 What volume of this acid should be diluted up to 1 litre to give 1 Molar acid (assume 100% purity)?

SAFETY TIP

Water is less dense than concentrated sulphuric acid, so if you pour a little water onto the acid the water floats on top. The heat of the reaction makes it boil and spit dangerously.

Because of this, concentrated sulphuric acid is always diluted by pouring the acid slowly into the water, where it mixes as it sinks to the bottom.

Questions

1 In some experiments on air, carbon dioxide is removed by bubbling the air through sodium hydroxide solution. Why is it then bubbled through concentrated sulphuric acid before passing on to the main experiment?

2 Why would it not be a good idea to mix concentrated sulphuric acid with methanoic acid (HCOOH) in an open flask? (Think about the product ...)

Summary

- Concentrated sulphuric acid is an important dehydrating agent.
- It is used for drying gases.
- It is also used to take the elements of water out of some organic chemicals.

Sulphuric acid may corrode many metals, but if used carefully it can help to protect aluminium from corrosion.

Aluminium's protective trick

You know that aluminium is a very reactive metal. It is above iron and zinc in the reactivity series. Indeed, it is so reactive that it can only be obtained from its molten ore by electrolysis.

a **Why can't aluminium be made by carbon reduction in a blast furnace, like iron?**

Yet aluminium is used all over the world for drink cans, take-away food containers and foil wrap for cooking. It seems to remain as shiny and untarnished as an unreactive metal such as gold or silver. Indeed, discarded aluminium cans can be a big problem in the environment, as they can take decades or longer to corrode away.

b **Why are steel-based 'tin' cans less of an environmental problem in the long term?**

So how can aluminium be so reactive yet appear to be quite the reverse? The answer is in the way it corrodes. Aluminium quickly forms an oxide layer in air, but this layer sticks tightly to the metal and effectively seals it off from further reaction.

aluminium + oxygen → aluminium oxide

c **Balance this equation:** $Al + O_2 \rightarrow Al_2O_3$

Strengthening the oxide layer

The protection given by aluminium's oxide layer depends in part on how thick it is. Fortunately the layer can be thickened artificially to make aluminium highly resistant to corrosion. The process used to do this is called **anodising**.

An aluminium object is anodised by connecting it as the positive electrode in an electrolytic cell with sulphuric acid.

d **Which electrode do you think is called the anode, the positive or the negative one?**

A discarded can takes decades to break down.

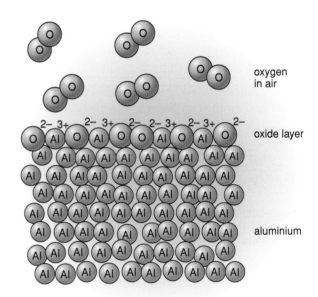

Aluminium's protective oxide layer.

Practical anodising

Stage 1: The aluminium object must first have its oxide layer cleaned off. This is done chemically, using strong hot sodium hydroxide solution which reacts with and dissolves the oxide – it will also dissolve the metal if left in for too long!

e Why should you not clean aluminium saucepans with oven cleaner containing sodium hydroxide?

Stage 2: The aluminium is then washed clean with distilled water and connected as the positive electrode in a tank of dilute sulphuric acid. The negative electrode may be made of lead.

Stage 3: A current is passed. The reaction is complex, but oxygen is produced on the surface of the aluminium anode. Some of this reacts with the aluminium to make a new oxide coating. The longer the current is passed, the thicker the coating becomes.

Stage 4: After the anodising process is complete, the aluminium is taken out and washed with water again. At this stage the oxide layer is quite porous. If it is put into a suitable dye, the dye molecules penetrate the layer and colour it.

Stage 5: The oxide layer is finally hardened and sealed by putting it into boiling water. If dye has been added, this is now permanently sealed in. The anodised object is now ready for use.

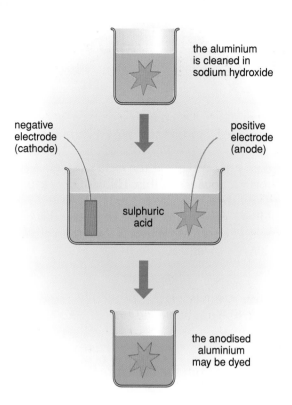

How aluminium is anodised.

This mountain bike frame is lightweight and strong as it is made from aluminium. It is also highly corrosion resistant and brightly coloured as it has been anodised and dyed.

Questions

1   Draw an annotated flow chart for the production of an anodised aluminium object.

2   What gas is likely to be produced at the negative electrode of the anodising cell?

3   If the aluminium was connected up as the negative terminal by mistake, do you think that the oxide layer would get thinner or thicker? Explain your answer.

4   You need a current of about half an amp for every 10 cm² of aluminium to be anodised. Approximately what current would be needed to anodise a 10 cm diameter aluminium disc?

5   Anodising works best at low temperatures. What problem might you encounter if you tried to anodise a large object?

Summary

- Aluminium is resistant to corrosion because of its protective oxide layer.

- This oxide layer can be made thicker and stronger by a process called anodising.

- For this process, the aluminium object is connected up as the positive electrode in an electrolytic cell containing dilute sulphuric acid.

Many of the common uses of metals, in construction or for machinery, rely on the fact that metals can be shaped easily but are very strong. Iron, usually in the form of **steel**, is so important because of this. Think of how much iron and steel is in use around the world in buildings, cars, trains, ships, bridges, railway lines, and so on. More iron is used than all other metals put together!

a Why do you think concrete for modern buildings is poured over steel rods, as shown in the photograph?

Even concrete has a heart of steel...

What is steel?

Iron straight from the blast furnace can be poured into moulds to make **cast iron**. This is hard, and was used to build some early bridges, but is too brittle for most uses. This is because it contains impurities such as phosphorus and silicon, as well as a small amount of carbon.

To make this iron more useful it must be turned into steel, which is a carefully blended mixture called an **alloy**. Usually, alloys are mixtures of different metals, but in most steel, iron is alloyed with just a small amount of carbon.

b Why can't cast iron be used to make car bodies?

Cast iron was used to build the Iron Bridge in Shropshire.

Making steel

As iron from the blast furnace already contains more carbon than is needed to make steel, this must first be removed. This is done by blowing oxygen at high pressure through the molten iron. This burns off the carbon, giving carbon monoxide and some carbon dioxide, which are carried out in the exhaust gases.

$$\text{carbon} + \text{oxygen} \rightarrow \text{carbon monoxide}$$
$$2C + O_2 \rightarrow 2CO$$

c The carbon is oxidised here; what is reduced? Add 'RedOx' arrows to your equation.

Once the carbon has been removed, a precisely controlled quantity of carbon can be added to produce high-quality steel. The whole furnace is then tipped and the molten steel is poured out.

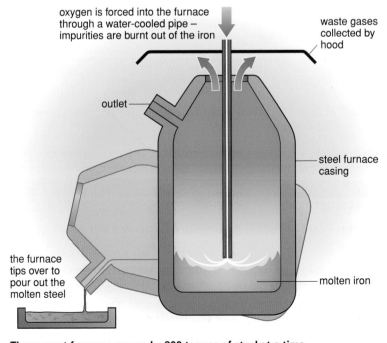

oxygen is forced into the furnace through a water-cooled pipe – impurities are burnt out of the iron

waste gases collected by hood

outlet

steel furnace casing

the furnace tips over to pour out the molten steel

molten iron

These great furnaces can make 300 tonnes of steel at a time.

Removing the phosphorus and silicon

The carbon is removed as a gaseous oxide, but what of the other impurities? The blast of oxygen converts both phosphorus and silicon to their oxides, but these do not come out in the waste gases. Instead, they have to be removed chemically.

These oxides are acidic oxides: they act like a dehydrated acid. Because of this they can be made to react with a base:

acid oxide + base → salt

d What acid oxide would you get if you dehydrated silicic acid, H_2SiO_3?

The base used is limestone (calcium carbonate), so carbon dioxide is also produced and comes off with the waste gases. For example, with silica (SiO_2):

silica + calcium → calcium + carbon
       carbonate   silicate   dioxide
SiO_2 + $CaCO_3$ → $CaSiO_3$ + CO_2

e Write a word equation for the reaction of phosphorous oxide with limestone. Why is water not one of the products?

The calcium silicate and phosphate form a low-density slag which floats on top of the molten steel and can be easily removed.

f This waste slag can be used by the fertiliser industry. Explain why.

Molten iron from the blast furnace is poured into a giant steel furnace. Some recycled scrap iron may also be added at this stage.

Questions

1 Why must the waste gases from the steel furnace be collected and not allowed to seep back into the factory?

2 Iron reacts with oxygen. Why does the oxygen blasted into the furnace react with the carbon and not the iron?

3 Solid 'pig iron' from a distant blast furnace *can* be used in a steel furnace. It is more usual to have the two furnaces close together, however, so that molten iron can be poured directly into the steel furnace, as in the photograph. Why is this the preferred method?

Summary

- Steel is an alloy of iron with a small amount of carbon.

- The excess carbon in the iron from a blast furnace is burnt out using a jet of oxygen.

- Other impurities are oxidised to acid oxides which are removed in an acid–base reaction with limestone.

Pure iron is actually fairly soft and not very strong, so a small amount of carbon is added to turn it into steel. The amount of carbon used depends on the job for which the steel is to be used.

How much carbon?

Low-carbon steel is still very soft and easy to shape. But adding only 1% of carbon to pure steel trebles its strength and makes it much harder.

With about 0.4% carbon, **mild steel** is easy to shape. It can be rolled into thin sheets for a wide variety of uses, from 'tin' cans to ships' hulls. It can also be pressed into shape for car bodies.

With nearer 0.8% carbon, **medium steel** is harder and is strong enough for use in spanners, hammers or axe heads.

Above 1% carbon, however, the strength drops a little, while the hardness still increases. Scissors, knives, chisels, files and drill bits benefit from this **high-carbon steel,** as they 'keep their edge' – but they may snap if badly used.

a Which steel should be used to make a crowbar? Explain your answer.

b Masonry drills have to be extra hard to drill through concrete. Why should you always wear safety goggles when using them? (What other property accompanies increasing hardness?)

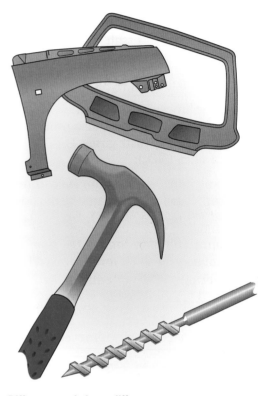

Different steels have different uses.

Heat treatment

Under a microscope, metals can be seen to be made of tightly interlocking crystals. Their properties depend on this crystal structure. The structure of steel changes if it is heated, and this is used to change its properties.

◆ **Quenching:** the steel is made red-hot and then cooled rapidly in cold water. This makes it hard but brittle.

◆ **Annealing:** if it is then reheated and allowed to cool slowly, it becomes soft and bendable again.

◆ **Tempering:** if the steel is heated until it turns light brown and is then quenched, it becomes tough and springy.

c A forester retrieved his axe head from a burnt-out tool shed, but when he tried to use it the edge of the blade dented and wouldn't cut.
  i Explain what had happened.
  ii What should he have done before using this axe head?
  iii Why mustn't he get it red hot? (What might happen?)

Adding other metals

Adding other metals can further change the properties of steel.

d Which metal might be added to steel used in a clockwork toy?

e Railway points have to be really strong and tough. Which metal is added to the steel for these?

f Which type of steel alloy might be used for pipes in a sulphuric acid plant?

g Drill bits must be very hard to drill through steel, and may get very hot. Which alloy could be used for this?

More than just a mixture

Iron and steel have one great weakness – they rust. Chromium is a transition metal that resists corrosion well. If you mix just 15% or so of chromium into molten steel, you get an alloy which is almost completely resistant to corrosion – stainless steel.

This may seem logical, but it is important to realise that the properties of alloys are not simply 'averages' of those of the metals from which they are made. Alloys may show completely different properties. For example, lead melts at 327°C, tin at 232°C, yet together they make solder which melts as low as 183°C.

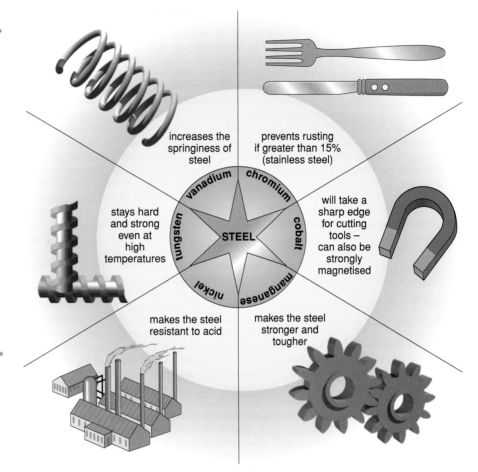

increases the springiness of steel

prevents rusting if greater than 15% (stainless steel)

stays hard and strong even at high temperatures

will take a sharp edge for cutting tools – can also be strongly magnetised

makes the steel resistant to acid

makes the steel stronger and tougher

vanadium chromium tungsten STEEL cobalt nickel manganese

Adding different metals changes the properties of steel.

Questions

1 Cast iron is still used for some things such as manhole covers because it is cheaper than steel. Why is it cheaper?

2 Scrap iron is often added to steel furnaces to save money by recycling. What problems might arise in the manufacture of specialist steels if too much scrap steel is added?

Summary

- The properties of steel vary according to the amount of carbon that is used.

- The properties of steel can also be greatly enhanced by adding other metals such as manganese.

- Stainless steel is an alloy with chromium.

Rusting is a big problem with iron and steel. To prevent steel car bodies and bridges from rusting away, they have to be painted to stop the oxygen and water getting at the metal. Alternatively, stainless steel can be made by mixing the molten metal with chromium. But chromium is much rarer and so more expensive than iron.

a Car exhaust systems are susceptible to rusting and the better ones are made from stainless steel. Suggest why this is not used for most exhausts.

A third method involves covering the steel with a thin coating of another metal, such as tin, which is less reactive than iron. This can act as a barrier like paint but is much longer lasting. This thin coat is usually formed by **electroplating** the steel.

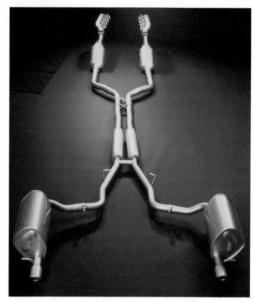

A stainless steel exhaust system.

How electroplating works

During electrolysis, any positive metal ions in the electrolyte are drawn towards the negative electrode. There they lose their charge and turn back into the metal. This is how aluminium is obtained from its molten ore, for example.

b Write the half-equation for the discharge of aluminium ions (3^+) at the negative electrode of an electrolytic cell.

This process can be simply adapted for electroplating. To tin-plate steel for tin cans, the steel is placed in an electrolytic cell containing an aqueous solution of a tin salt as the electrolyte. The steel is then connected as the negative electrode and a current passed.

Positive tin ions are attracted to the negative steel plate and are discharged. The tin atoms form a thin but even and strongly attached layer over the surface.

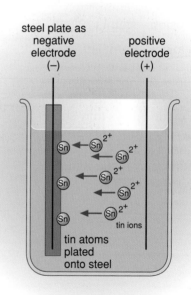

Metal ions are attracted to the negative electrode.

$$Sn^{2+} + 2e^- \xrightarrow{\text{on the negative steel plate}} Sn$$

If the positive electrode is made of tin, these atoms will lose electrons and go into solution as ions to replace those being plated at the negative electrode.

c Write an equation for what happens to the tin atoms at the positive electrode.

Silver and gold plating

Tin plating is done purely to protect the iron, but sometimes precious metals are plated onto base metals such as steel or nickel. This can give them an expensive appearance at a fraction of the price of the precious metals alone.

Before high-quality stainless steel became widely available in the last century, silver was often plated onto nickel for affordable cutlery sets that did not tarnish.

d This silver plated nickel-ware is often stamped with the letters EPNS. What do you think they stand for?

As for tin or zinc plating, the article to be electroplated is connected as the negative electrode in an electrolytic cell. In this case a solution of silver salts containing silver ions (Ag^+) is used as the electrolyte.

Silver-plated nickel is cheaper than solid silver.

Chromium plating

Chromium gives a shiny, mirror-like, rustproof surface when plated onto steel. It is cheaper than stainless steel, as only a thin layer is needed. Chromium plating was very popular on American cars in the 1950s and is still used today for a range of uses, including bicycle handlebars!

Unfortunately, chromium doesn't stick very well if plated directly onto steel. Instead a thin layer of copper is plated first, followed by nickel and then chromium for a durable finish.

e What electrolyte could be used for copper plating?

Shiny chromium-plating was a big hit in America in the 1950s.

Questions

Galvanised steel is protected by a thin coating of zinc.

1 Describe how you could galvanise steel by electroplating the steel.

2 What electrolyte could you use?

3 Write a half-equation for the reaction of the Zn^{2+} ions at the negative electrode.

4 What would you use for the positive electrode and why?

5 Are the positive ions oxidised or reduced as they are plated onto the steel? Explain your answer.

Summary

- Steel (and other metals) may be electroplated with a thin layer of another metal.

- They are connected as the negative electrode in an electrolytic cell.

- The electrolyte is a solution containing the positive metal ions to be plated.

The American F22 fighter plane has been designed to be the best fighter aircraft in the world. In order to do that, it must be able to outperform all others – fly faster, be more agile and more manoeuvrable.

All this extra performance will put enormous strain on the body and wings. These extra forces are enough to tear apart a traditional aluminium alloy structure. So it's not surprising that the designers turned to a different metal, titanium, for many of the key parts of this new plane.

So why is titanium so good?

◆ It's as strong as steel, yet has only half the density – which is vital in aircraft construction.

◆ It has a very high melting point (nearly 2000°C) and so can cope with the effects of frictional heating caused when flying at high speed.

a Why is low density so important in aircraft construction?

Flying much faster than sound puts an enormous strain on the F22, so super-strong titanium alloys are needed.

Instant protection

Another key property of titanium is that it is highly reactive and combines instantly with the oxygen in the air. That last reason may seem a little odd yet, strangely enough, that very reactivity makes pure titanium almost totally resistant to rust or corrosion. The instant it comes into contact with air, it reacts to form a thin but very tough oxide layer, which prevents further damage. It will even reseal itself if scratched!

b Which common metal shares this property?

This corrosion-proof property has led to titanium finding many important uses. In nuclear power stations, for example, it is used for the pipes that carry steam from the reactors to drive the generators, and in the condensers that turn the steam back to water for recycling. It is also used for piping in conventional power stations where sea water is used as a coolant, which would eventually rust even stainless steel.

Titanium is also used in that most corrosive of environments – inside the human body!

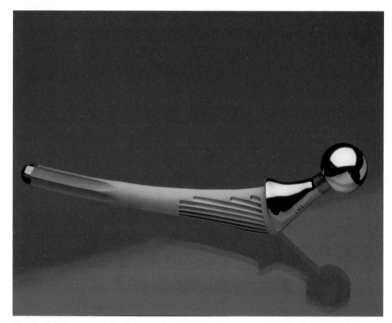

The ball joints used for hip replacement surgery are made from titanium. They are very strong and are not attacked by corrosive body fluids.

Refining titanium

Titanium is a relatively common metal (0.6% of the Earth's crust), yet it is more difficult to mine and extract than other common metals.

Its oxide ore, rutile (titanium dioxide, TiO_2), is hard and resistant and so collects in sand. The most important titanium-bearing sands are found on beaches in Australia. Yet even here, the rutile amounts to only 1% of the sand, so it is quite expensive to separate out.

Once obtained, titanium's high reactivity makes it very hard to extract. You might think it could be melted and obtained by electrolysis, like aluminium, but the very high melting point of rutile makes this uneconomic.

c Why does a high melting point cause such a problem?

Instead, the titanium oxide is first converted to titanium tetrachloride ($TiCl_4$). This is then reacted with sodium or magnesium in a thermit reaction. The more reactive metal pushes the titanium from its compound, giving out large amounts of energy in the process.

$$TiCl_4 + 4Na \rightarrow Ti + 4NaCl + energy$$

d Write word and balanced equations for the reaction of magnesium with titanium tetrachloride.

Even this has its problems. If the reaction were run in an open container, the hot titanium would immediately react with oxygen from the air to form titanium dioxide again. So further expense is added, as the whole process has to take place in sealed units filled with an inert gas such as helium or argon.

A strip of refined titanium metal in a heap of rutile ore – not easy to extract!

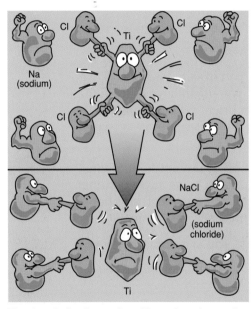
Titanium is finally produced by a thermit reaction.

Questions

1 Draw a flow chart for the production of titanium from rutile-bearing sands.

2 Suggest another metal that could be used to extract titanium from titanium tetrachloride.

3 Titanium tetrachloride can be made by dissolving rutile in concentrated hydrochloric acid.

   a What type of reaction is this?

   b Write word and balanced equations for this reaction.

Summary

• Titanium is a very useful metal because it is strong and resistant to corrosion.

• It also has a low density and a high melting point.

• It is harder to extract from its ore than most common metals.

It is often very important to know what metal ions are present in an unknown compound or solution. For example:

◆ Miners need to know what's in the rocks they are digging up.

◆ Factories need to check any waste water they let out into rivers, to ensure that it doesn't contain any dangerous pollutants.

◆ Soil scientists need to check soils to see whether they have enough of the minerals needed for good plant growth.

Fortunately there are some simple tests that can be used to identify the common metals.

Sodium's calling card

Have you ever seen a pan of salted water boil over during cooking? If so, you might have noticed that the gas flame turned a bright yellow-orange as the water sprayed through it. This colour is caused by sodium ions in the salt solution.

In fact, the light given off by excited sodium ions is so bright that it is used for some street lighting. But as it is such a unique colour, it can also be used as a test for the presence of sodium.

a What colour would you see if you sprayed sea water through a flame?

Flame tests

To test for sodium in the laboratory, a platinum wire is first cleaned in concentrated hydrochloric acid. It is then dipped into the powder to be tested to pick up a small sample and held in a medium Bunsen burner flame. Any sodium ions present become excited and give off the characteristic yellow-orange colour.

Some other metals also show characteristic colours in this test:

◆ potassium gives a pale lilac flame

◆ lithium gives a scarlet flame

◆ calcium gives a red flame

◆ barium gives a green flame.

b Why do you think lithium and barium salts are sometimes used in fireworks?

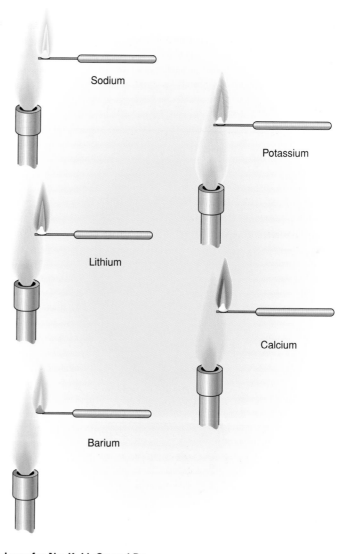

Colours for Na, K, Li, Ca and Ba.

Which bonds?

Although **infrared spectrographs** can be very complex, some bonds give very clear markers that can be easily identified. The table shows some important examples.

c Ethanol (C_2H_5OH) contains C–H bonds, a C–C bond, a C–O bond and an O–H bond. Locate these markers on the vodka spectrograph.

This simple pattern rarely works out so easily, however. Propanone (CH_3COCH_3) has a C=O double bond which clearly shows up on its printout.

d Locate propanone's C=O trough on the spectrograph below.

You may also be able to spot the slight dip caused by C–H bonds stretching, but where do the other spikes come from? Unfortunately C–H bonds bend in different ways in different compounds, and these particular dips are peculiar to propanone.

But this very uniqueness can be turned to an advantage, given a huge database and lots of computing power. That's why this part of the spectrum is sometimes called the 'fingerprint zone'.

bond type	stretch or bend	wavenumber range (cm^{-1})
C–H	stretch	2800–3000
C–H	bend	850–1500 (very variable)
O–H	stretch	3200–3600
O–H	bend	1260–1410
C–O	stretch	1040–1150
C=O	stretch	1700–1740
C–C	stretch	700–800 (weak)
C=C	stretch	1620–1680

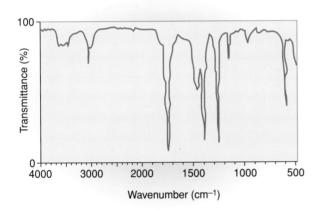

Infrared absorption spectrum of propanone.

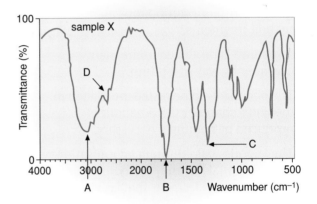

Infrared absorption spectrum of sample X.

Questions

Erica thinks that sample X (above right) could be a carboxylic acid, such as CH_3COOH; Carlton thinks it could be an alcohol, such as C_2H_5OH. Look carefully at the regions marked A–D. (You may need to draw structural diagrams of the two compounds so that you know which bonds to look out for.)

1 Which is the critical region and who does it suggest is correct?

2 Why are dips in region C difficult to work out?

3 Why is region C helpful if you have access to a database of spectrographs?

4 Which two features would be common to both alcohols and carboxylic acids and what are they?

Summary

• The bonds in organic chemicals absorb different infrared wavelengths as they stretch and bend.

• Infrared absorption spectrographs can be used to identify organic chemicals.

• Some individual bonds can be identified, but spectrographs usually have to be matched to standard spectrographs held on a vast database.

22:13 Mass spectrometry

Visible light spectroscopy lets us identify elements from billions of miles away in space as well as within the laboratory.

Infrared spectroscopy tells us about the bonding arrangements in organic molecules.

A third instrumental method of analysis allows us to identify minute traces of chemicals, less than a millionth of a gram. This is **mass spectrometry**, which works on very different principles.

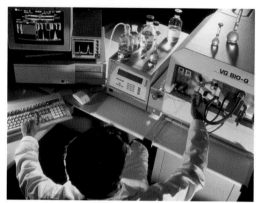

Using a mass spectrometer.

The mass spectrometer

Unlike the previous methods, a **mass spectrometer** works by testing the chemicals to destruction, ripping compounds apart and ionising their fragments.

- A vacuum is produced in the main chamber by way of a pump.

- The chemicals to be tested are placed in the entry chamber (A). A vapour is produced by heating if necessary.

- The vapours pass through an ionisation chamber (B). Here they are bombarded by high-speed electrons that knock electrons from the particles.

- The ions then pass through an accelerator (C), which fires them at high speed along the apparatus.

- The ions shoot through a zone (D) where a strong electromagnetic field can be applied. This makes them curve around.

- The ions are collected by a detector (E).

- This is linked to a chart printer that records the number of particles striking the detector for different strengths of the magnetic field.

a Draw an annotated diagram of a mass spectrometer to explain how it works.

b Look up krypton in the Periodic Table. What do you think the large bar at 84 might represent on this?

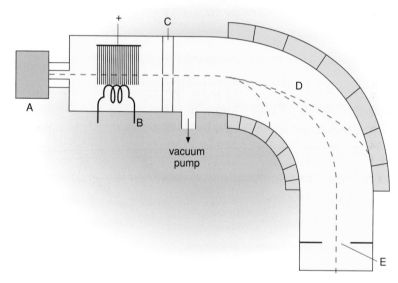

How a mass spectrometer works (see text).

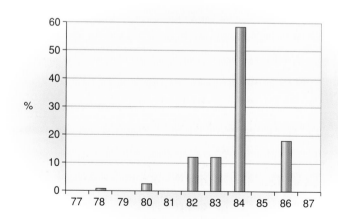

A mass spectrometer printout for krypton (Kr^+) ions.

Getting it right in industry

Steel furnaces use molten iron straight from the blast furnace plus up to 25% of scrap iron. This might contain various quantities of other metals, depending on the origin of the scrap. Yet modern steel alloys need to be made to precise proportions. How do you know how much manganese or vanadium to add to the mixture, for example, if you don't know how much is there already?

These days the answer is simple. A small sample is taken to the laboratory. This can then be run through a mass spectrometer or other instrument and the exact composition of your molten steel can be back within the hour. Traditional analytical techniques would have taken days!

b Why is speed so important?

Advancing medicine

New drugs cost hundreds of millions of pounds to develop, so drug companies are investing millions in the latest accelerated mass spectrometers to follow minute traces of new drugs around the human body and pinpoint their action as rapidly as possible.

Monitoring pollution

How do you know what atmospheric pollution is like in your area today? Simple – just go on the Internet and tap straight into the automated pollution monitoring station for your area. Direct data logging using specialised sensors has revolutionised the way we monitor our environment.

For more complex pollution issues, samples still need to be taken. But even here advanced instrumental techniques are speeding up the process and making it far more accurate. For example, there have been concerns that tiny traces of the sex hormone oestrogen used in the contraceptive pill have been getting into water supplies and affecting the fertility of fish – and maybe humans too. Recent research on Thames water using an incredibly sensitive mass spectrometer has indeed shown the presence of oestrogen, but has also proved that it is of natural origin and is not linked to the pill.

Instrumental analysis allows precise alloys to be made.

Sex hormones found in the Thames appear to have a natural origin.

Questions

1 Brainstorm a list of all the possible uses for instrumental analysis.

2 Locate your local atmospheric pollution data on the Internet at www.heinemann.co.uk/hotlinks then type in Express Code 2059P and click on this activity. Click on 'data and statistics' followed by 'get data now'. Choose the type of information you want, then follow the menus to select the type of pollutant and location.

Summary

- Instrumental analysis methods are now widely used, since they are fast, sensitive and accurate.

- They are vital to scientific research, industrial production, health care and environmental monitoring.

End of module questions

1 This diagram shows the manufacturing process for sulphuric acid.

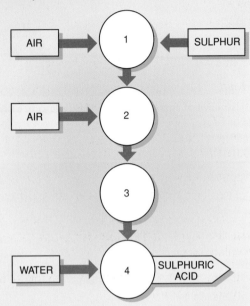

a What product is formed in stage 1? Write a balanced chemical equation for this.

b In stage 2 this is oxidised to sulphur trioxide: how is the reaction speeded up?

c The stage 2 reaction is reversible and the forward reaction is exothermic. Explain why this reaction cannot simply be run at a higher temperature to make it go faster.

d Sulphur trioxide dissolves in water to form sulphuric acid. Explain why in stage 3 the sulphur trioxide is dissolved in concentrated sulphuric acid instead, which must then be watered down in stage 4.

e Write a balanced chemical equation for the reaction of sulphur trioxide with water.

f Explain how sulphuric acid is used in the manufacture of fertilisers.

2 Aluminium is a very reactive metal.

a Explain why aluminium foil stays so shiny and does not corrode.

b Explain how anodising can make aluminium even more resistant to corrosion. Draw a circuit diagram to show how anodising is done, labelling the positive and negative electrodes.

c What other advantage does anodised aluminium have?

3 Steel is an alloy of iron and <1.5% of carbon.

a Iron from the blast furnace contains 2–3% of carbon. Describe how this is removed in the first stage of steel production.

b Explain why this process also removes impurities such as sulphur and phosphorus but does not remove any silicon.

c Explain how any silicon (in the form of silicon oxide) is removed from the iron. Write an equation for this reaction.

d What percentage of carbon would then be added to make mild steel for car bodies?

e What percentage of carbon would then be added to make knife blades?

f Why is chromium often added to the steel made for knife blades?

4 Steel can be electroplated with zinc – galvanised – to protect it from rusting.

a Draw a circuit diagram to show how a piece of steel could be galvanised. Mark in the positive and negative electrodes.

b What would be a suitable electrolyte to use?

c Write a 'half equation' to show what happens to the zinc ions during electroplating.

5 Titanium is a relatively common metal in the Earth's crust.

a What is the common ore of titanium and where is it found?

b If titanium is common, why is it so expensive?

c Draw an annotated flow diagram for the industrial manufacture of titanium, starting from ore-rich sand.

d Write a balanced chemical equation for the final thermit reaction with sodium.

e What key properties of titanium make it so useful for high performance aircraft?

f What key properties of titanium make it so useful for hip replacement ball joints?

6 Jenny, Alex and Bashir tested some unknown chemicals. Identify them from the results of the tests they performed, explaining your reasoning.

a Jenny performed a flame test on an unknown white powder. It gave an apple-green flame. She then dissolved some of the powder in water to form a clear solution and added this to some acidified silver nitrate solution. A white precipitate formed. The solution gave no reaction with barium chloride solution, however.

b Alex also had an unknown white powder. This did not give a very clear flame test until viewed through blue glass, when a lilac flame was seen. She also dissolved some of the powder in water to form a clear solution and added this to some acidified barium chloride solution. A white precipitate formed.

c Bashir had a green powder to identify. This gave a blue-green flame test. It would not dissolve in water, but did dissolve in sulphuric acid, fizzing rapidly and leaving a blue solution. The gas that formed turned lime water milky.

7 Spectroscopy is a very important analytical tool.

a Visible light spectroscopy uses a glass prism. What does this do to the different wavelengths of light?

b What would you see if you passed light from a sodium flame test through a prism and onto a screen?

c Small traces of sodium often mask out the weak potassium colour in a flame test. Explain how spectroscopy overcomes this problem.

d The spectrograph from the Sun shows several dark lines – like the negative image of a flame test. Explain why this happens.

e Flame test colours are given off or absorbed as electrons change energy levels. What happens when infrared radiation is absorbed by a molecule?

8 This question is about mass spectrometry.

a Describe in your own words how a mass spectrometer works. Make sure you include all of the important stages. You might want to use a simple analogy to explain why lighter particles are deflected more than heavy ones.

b Krypton is a monatomic gas. Explain why its mass spectrograph shows more than one bar.

c Fluorine has just one isotope, yet the mass spectrograph of fluorine shows two bars. Explain why.

d Explain why large organic chemicals give several different bars.

e Chlorine has two isotopes, ^{35}Cl (75%) and ^{37}Cl (25%). Sketch the mass spectrograph chlorine would give for Cl^+ atoms only. Show the relative size of the bars as well as their mass numbers.

f Cl_2^+ bars would also show up. How many bars would show for these molecular ions, and what would their mass numbers be?

Extended homework questions

1 Brass is an important alloy made from copper and zinc. The graph shows how the properties change as different amounts of tin are mixed into the copper.

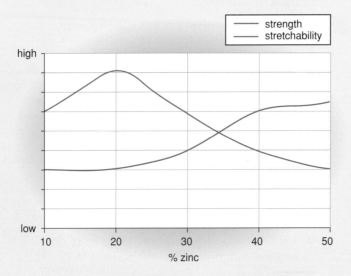

a A firm has been asked to make brass ship fitments for the navy using 40% zinc. Zinc is cheaper than copper and the firm now wants to increase its profit margin by using 45% zinc. The brass needs to be as strong as possible. From the graph, will it be able to 'get away' with this? Give reasons for your answer.

b The same firm is also considering making brass shell cases for the army. These need to be stretched into shape. Will it be able to use brass containing 45% zinc for this? Explain your answer and advise the firm on the best 'mix' for this job.

2 Seashells are very pretty but they are soft and soon go dull, so they are not good for jewellery. Not any more! Silver-plated seashells are now available as earrings, pendants and brooches… And it is all thanks to a black carbon-rich paint which sticks well to the shells and also conducts electricity.

Explain carefully how you could use:
- silver nitrate solution
- a power pack
- some wire and crocodile clips
- the special carbon paint
- small seashells
- a carbon rod

to make beautiful seashell jewellery.

3 Guy set up a spectrometer so that it pointed towards a firework display on November 5th. He took a photograph of the spectrum produced by a particularly spectacular red and green display. He then compared this to some flame test results he had photographed earlier.

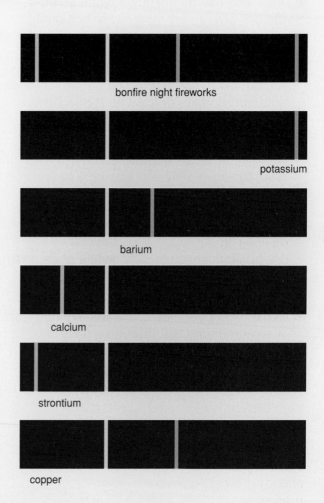

a What is the strong yellow line that crops up in all the spectrographs, and how did it get there?

b Help Guy to identify the metals used for these fireworks.

c Guy didn't see any lilac fireworks, so why do you think he got a potassium line?
(Hint: many fireworks contain gunpowder.)

Where is an object's centre of mass? The drawings show some examples. Notice that, for a symmetrical object such as a sphere or a bowl, the centre of mass lies on its axis of symmetry. (This is because equal amounts of its mass lie on either side of the axis.)

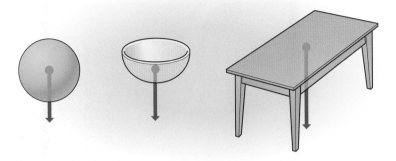

The position of the centre of mass for several objects. For the table, the centre of mass is in the air below the table-top.

a Where is the centre of mass of a cylinder?

b Picture a solid cone. Where do you think its centre of mass is?

Finding the centre of mass

The diagrams show how to find the centre of mass of an irregularly shaped piece of thin card. This method uses the idea that, when an object hangs freely from a point, its centre of mass lies directly below the point of suspension. If the object swings, it will come to rest with its centre of mass below the point of suspension.

◆ Hang the card from a pin. Make sure it is free to swing.

◆ Use a plumb-line from the pin to mark the card with a vertical line. (Mark points along the line.) The centre of mass lies on this line.

◆ Hang the card from a different point. Mark the vertical line.

◆ Repeat once more, from a different point.

◆ Now use a ruler to draw straight lines through the marked points. The lines should cross at a single point, the centre of mass.

c Why is this point the centre of mass?

Questions

1 What is meant by the centre of mass of an object?

2 Where is the centre of mass of each of the following objects? Which has a centre of mass that is in the air?

   a a book

   b a CD

   c a person (roughly).

3 Where is the centre of mass of a 1 litre carton of milk? How will its centre of mass change as you drink the milk? And where will it be when the carton is empty?

This high jumper curves her body as she passes over the bar. Her centre of mass actually passes under the bar.

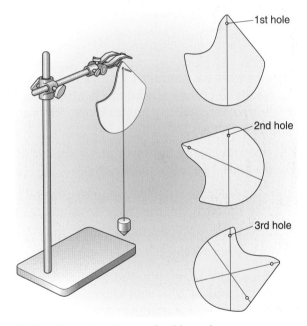

Finding the centre of mass of a thin card.

Summary

• The weight of a body acts at its centre of mass.

• A freely suspended object will hang with its centre of mass vertically below the point of suspension.

Weightlifters need a good sense of balance. If the weights tip to one side, they become unbalanced and fall to the floor. It's harder if the weights on the two ends of the pole are unequal, and harder still if you use only one arm.

If the weights are symmetrical, it's easy – the centre of mass is at the midpoint of the bar, and this is where it balances. If the weights are unequal, try further along the bar, closer to the heavier weights.

You can understand this by thinking about the **turning effect** (or **moment**) of each of the weights.

◆ The weights on the left tend to turn the bar anticlockwise about the pivot; they have an anticlockwise moment.

◆ The weights on the right tend to turn the bar clockwise; they have a clockwise moment.

For the weights to be balanced, the heavier weights must be closer to the pivot. This should remind you of the two factors that determine the moment of a force:

◆ the size of the force

◆ the distance between the pivot and the line of action of the force.

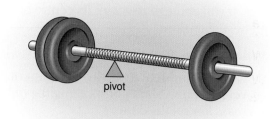

To keep the bar balanced, the pivot must be nearer the heavier weight.

Defining moment

The greater the force, and the greater its distance from the pivot, the greater its moment. This tells us how to calculate the moment of a force:

moment = force × perpendicular distance between pivot and line of action of force

Since force is measured in newtons (N) and distance in metres (m), moment is measured in newton-metres (Nm).

a The diagram shows a force of 50 N whose line of action is at 0.2 m from the pivot. Calculate the moment of this force. Does it act in a clockwise or anticlockwise direction?

The right angle

When calculating the moment of a force, it is essential to multiply the force by the correct distance. The following worked example shows how to find the distance from the pivot to the line of action of the force.

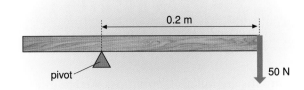

The moment of a force depends on its size and its distance from the pivot.

Worked example

Find the moment of the 10 N force about the pivot.

◆ Extend the force arrow to show the line of action of the force.

◆ Draw a line from the pivot that meets the line of action at 90°.

◆ Measure or calculate the length of this line.

In the diagram, the force acts on the bar at 0.5 m from the pivot, but the distance we require is 0.4 m.

moment of force = 10 N × 0.4 m = 4 Nm

b What is the moment of a force that passes through the pivot?

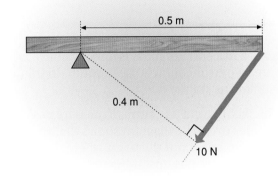

Diagram for worked example.

Questions

1 What are the units of force, distance and moment?

2 Which has a greater moment, a force of 10 N acting at a distance of 3 m from a pivot, or a force of 8 N acting at 4 m from the pivot?

3 Explain how a heavy adult can balance a much lighter child on a seesaw. Use the idea of *moment of a force* in your answer.

4 Which of the three forces in the diagram has the greatest moment about the pivot? Explain your answer.

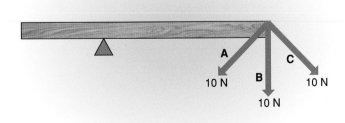

Summary

- The moment of a force equals the force (in newtons) times the perpendicular distance (in metres) between the pivot and the line of action of the force.

- Moment is measured in newton-metres (Nm).

Humans are tall, thin creatures. We are inherently unstable. We can remain upright by standing with our centre of mass directly above our feet.

When we walk, we lift one foot from the ground and start tipping forward. Before we can topple over, we move our free foot forwards, and regain our balance. Toddlers find this very difficult at first.

To avoid falling over, this child must keep her centre of mass above her feet.

Balance

You can stand a pen or pencil on its end. It remains upright, because its centre of mass is directly above its base (the point or area where it contacts the ground). In this position, the pen is described as **stable**.

Tip it slightly, and its centre of mass moves beyond its base. Now it topples over. The diagram shows that the weight of the pen now has a moment about the point where the pen pivots. In this tilted position, the pen is unstable.

An object will tend to tip over if the line of action of its weight lies outside its base. To have greatest stability, an object should have a large base and a low centre of mass.

a A plant is growing in a pot. Explain why it becomes more unstable as it grows taller. Use diagrams to support your answer.

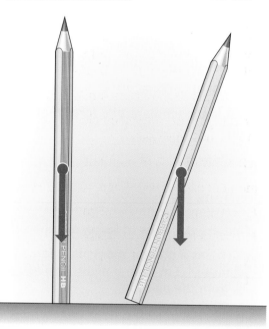

The upright pencil is stable; tilt it a little and it topples over.

The law of moments

If an object is balanced, the turning effects of the forces on it must cancel each other out. We can summarise this idea in an equation:

$$\text{moment of clockwise forces} = \text{moment of anticlockwise forces}$$

The two worked examples show how to use this idea.

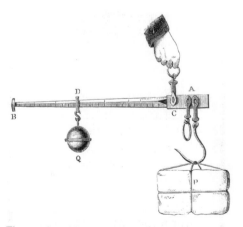

The steelyard is an ingenious weighing device that makes use of the law of moments. Invented in Arabia over 2000 years ago, it is still in widespread use around the world. The object to be weighed hangs from a hook; weights are moved along the beam to make it balance.

Worked example 1

The beam shown in the diagram is balanced. Calculate the size of force F.

Step 1 Identify the clockwise and anticlockwise forces:

F is tending to turn the beam clockwise; the 20 N force acts anticlockwise.

Step 2 Apply the law of moments:

moment of clockwise force = moment of anticlockwise force

$F \times 0.4\text{ m} = 20\text{ N} \times 0.5\text{ m}$

$F = 20 \times 0.5 / 0.4 = 25\text{ N}$

You can probably see that this is a reasonable answer. F acts closer to the pivot than the 20 N force, so it must be greater than 20 N if it is to balance its effect.

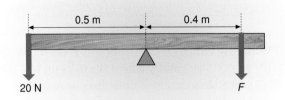

Diagram for worked example 1.

Worked example 2

Here is a slightly different situation. The beam is balanced, but the pivot is no longer at its midpoint. This time, the force F acts to balance the weight of the beam.

Step 1 Identify the clockwise and anticlockwise forces:

F is tending to turn the beam clockwise; the weight of the beam (5 N) acts anticlockwise.

Step 2 Apply the law of moments:

moment of clockwise force = moment of anticlockwise force

$F \times 0.2\text{ m} = 5\text{ N} \times 0.3\text{ m}$

$F = 5 \times 0.3 / 0.2 = 7.5\text{ N}$

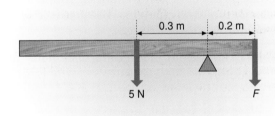

Diagram for worked example 2.

b Explain why we did not have to worry about the weight of the beam in worked example 1.

Questions

1 Write the law of moments in the form of an equation.

2 Explain why double-decker buses have heavy weights attached beneath the floor of the lower deck.

3 A ruler, 1 m long, weighs 1.2 N. A student pivots it at the 25 cm mark.

   a What downward force is needed at the 0 cm end to balance the ruler?

   b What vertical force is needed at the 100 cm end to balance the ruler? (Take care to state its direction.)

4 A seesaw is pivoted at its midpoint. A child weighing 200 N sits at one end, 1.4 m from the pivot. How far from the pivot must a 350 N child sit to balance the seesaw?

Summary

- The law of moments states that, for an object to be balanced, the moment of clockwise forces equals the moment of anticlockwise forces.

- An object will tend to tip over if the line of action of its weight is outside its base.

The racing car in the photograph is travelling at speed around a tight bend. The road surface is not level but tilted or 'banked'. This helps vehicles to follow the curve of the road; without it, they would be in danger of sliding off.

This should remind you of an important law of motion: an object will continue to move in a straight line at a steady speed, unless an unbalanced force acts on it. So, if an object is to move along a curved path, a force must act on it to make it do so.

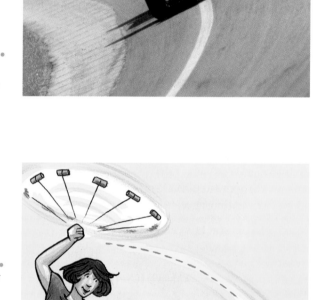

Round and round

If you tie a cork to a string and whirl it around your head, it moves in circles. The string is pulling on the cork, and the force of the string keeps it on its circular path. Let go of the string, and the cork flies off.

Although the cork may be moving round at a steady speed, its velocity is always changing, because its direction is always changing.

a Revision: What is the difference between speed and velocity?

Centripetal forces

Whenever an object is moving in a circle, you can try to identify the force that keeps it moving in the circle. Such a force is described as a **centripetal force**. Centripetal means *centre-seeking*.

For example, the Moon orbits the Earth. The pull of the Earth's gravity provides the centripetal force.

Another example is electrons orbiting the nucleus of an atom. The electrons have negative charge, and the nucleus is positive. The electrostatic attraction of the nucleus holds the electrons in their orbits.

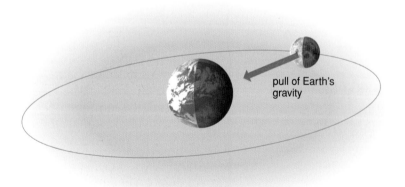

The pull of the string keeps the cork moving in a circular path – until you let go.

Stars orbit gradually around the centre of their galaxy. They are held in their orbits by the galaxy's gravitational pull.

pull of Earth's gravity

b What force holds the Earth in its orbit around the Sun?

The size of the force

A centripetal force must be just the right size to keep an object moving in a particular circle at the right speed. What does the size of the centripetal force depend on?

◆ The mass of the object: the greater the mass, the greater the force needed.

◆ The speed of the object: the faster it is moving, the greater the force needed.

◆ The radius of the circle: the smaller the radius, the greater the force needed.

c Which needs a greater centripetal force: a car moving slowly around a gentle bend, or the same car moving quickly around a sharper bend?

The hammer-thrower's muscles provide the centripetal force needed to move the hammer in a circle.

Questions

1 What do we call a force that acts on an object, pushing it towards the centre of a circle?

2 Which diagram, A, B or C, shows correctly the centripetal force acting on the aircraft as it follows a curved path? Explain why you have chosen this diagram.

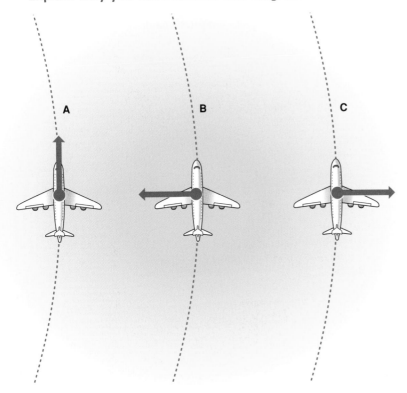

3 Jupiter is orbited by at least 30 moons, and astronomers keep finding new ones. What force holds them in their orbits around Jupiter?

4 What force holds electrons in their orbit around the nucleus of an atom?

5 As the hammer-thrower spins round (see photo), the hammer moves faster and faster. How does the thrower's pulling force change as the hammer speeds up?

Summary

• Any object moving in a circular path is acted on by a centripetal force, directed towards the centre of the circle.

The Earth is orbited by many spacecraft, such as the **satellite** network of the Global Positioning System (GPS). Some of these spacecraft are in circular orbits; others are in elliptical orbits. They are all held in their orbits by the pull of the Earth's gravity.

The right speed

How does gravity keep a spacecraft in its orbit? The diagram shows one spacecraft in a circular orbit.

The spacecraft that make up the GPS network travel in circular orbits around the Earth.

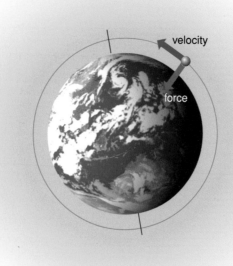

Velocity and centripetal force are at right angles to each other for an object travelling at a steady speed around a circular path.

◆ At any moment, the spacecraft's velocity is at a *tangent* to the orbit, and if it were not for the Earth's gravity, the spacecraft would continue in a straight line.

◆ The force of gravity is always pulling the spacecraft towards the centre of the Earth.

Force and velocity are represented by arrows on the diagram.

Now you can see why the spacecraft must travel at just the right speed to stay in its orbit. If it travels too fast, it will tend to move away from the Earth.

For a spacecraft orbiting a few hundred kilometres above the Earth's surface, the stable speed is about 8 km/s, or nearly 30 000 km/h.

a What would happen to the spacecraft if it slowed down?

Satellite data

The table shows information about four spacecraft in circular orbits around the Earth.

b Explain why spacecraft B requires a bigger centripetal force to keep it in its orbit than spacecraft A.

c Which of the spacecraft has the smallest centripetal force acting on it? Explain your answer.

d Copy the table, and extend it to include values for the spacecrafts' velocities. What pattern do you see in the values?

e A geostationary satellite orbits the Earth once every 24 hours. By drawing a suitable graph, and extending it, estimate the radius of its orbit.

Spacecraft	Mass (kg)	Radius of orbit (km)	Time for one orbit (hours)
A	200	7000	1.5
B	400	7000	1.5
C	200	15 000	4.7
D	200	30 000	13.3

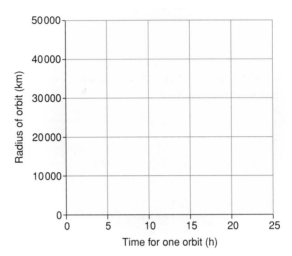

Suitable axes for the graph of question e.

Solar system

The planets orbiting the Sun form a system rather like the artificial Earth satellites we have just considered. They orbit at different distances. The further they are from the Sun, the weaker is the Sun's gravity, and so the slower they must travel to stay in their orbits.

Questions

1 A racing car travels around a track that forms a closed loop. As the car speeds around the bends, it relies on friction between its tyres and the road surface to provide the centripetal force that keeps it on its curved path.

The sideways forces between tyres and road throw up a lot of dust.

a If the car speeds up as it is travelling around a bend, must the centripetal force acting on it increase or decrease?

b The car reaches a tighter bend (smaller radius of curvature). Why might the driver slow down?

c On one bend, the road surface is greasy. Use the idea of centripetal force to explain why the driver should travel more slowly over this stretch of the track.

2 The Earth has many artificial satellites, orbiting at different distances. Suppose that a particular satellite is moved to a more distant orbit.

a Does the Earth's gravitational pull on it increase or decrease?

b How must the satellite's speed change if it is to stay in this new orbit?

Summary

• The centripetal force is greater:

– for an object of greater mass

– for a faster-moving object

– for a circle of smaller radius.

If you have ever pushed a heavily loaded trolley around a supermarket, you will know how difficult it can be to control. If the trolley is moving fast, it is difficult to slow it down or to make it change direction.

If you try to change the speed or direction of a trolley, you are trying to change its **momentum**. The momentum of an object depends on both its mass and its velocity.

Here is how to calculate momentum:

$$\text{momentum (kg m/s)} = \text{mass (kg)} \times \text{velocity (m/s)}$$

Heading for a soft landing.

Worked example

Calculate the momentum of a 20 kg shopping trolley moving at 5 m/s.

Write down the formula for momentum, and substitute values:

$$\text{momentum} = \text{mass} \times \text{velocity}$$

$$\text{momentum} = 20\,\text{kg} \times 5\,\text{m/s} = 100\,\text{kg m/s}$$

So the trolley's momentum is 100 kg m/s (100 kilogram metres per second). There is no special name for this unit.

Note that, to be complete, we should include the *direction* of an object's momentum. This is because momentum depends on velocity, which includes direction.

a Which has more momentum, a 40 kg boy running at 5 m/s, or his 60 kg parent running after him at 4 m/s? Who will win the race?

b A car travels at a steady speed around a bend in the road. Is its momentum changing? Explain your answer.

Snookered

If you play snooker, you'll have noticed a few things that may help you understand the idea of momentum. What happens when a moving ball collides head-on with an identical, stationary ball? The moving ball stops dead; the second ball moves off at the speed of the first ball, and in the same direction. All of the momentum of the first ball has been transferred to the second ball.

velocity = 5 m/s

mass = 20 kg

To calculate the trolley's momentum we need to know its mass and velocity.

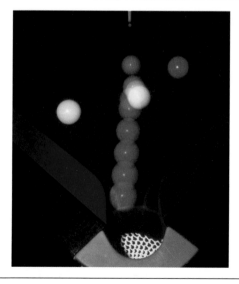

Now imagine a collision between two cars. One is moving at 20 m/s; it runs into the back of a stationary car of the same mass. The two cars stick together and move forward. We could predict that their speed will be 10 m/s. This is because the moving mass has doubled, so its speed has halved. In practice, this is unlikely to be exactly the case. However, you can do an experiment in the lab to show the same idea. One glider runs into another; magnets stick them together, and they move off at half the original speed.

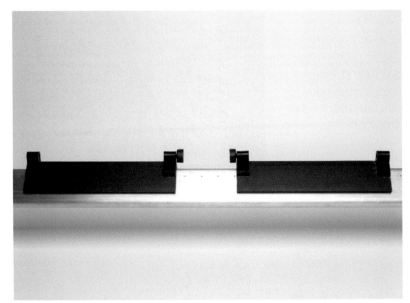

A linear air track is useful for investigating frictionless collisions. These gliders are fitted with magnets so that they bounce smoothly off one another, or stick firmly together.

c Make a prediction: what would happen if a trolley of mass 1 kg collided with a stationary trolley of mass 2 kg, and they stuck together? If the first trolley was moving at 6 m/s, at what speed do you think they would move off?

In these examples of collisions, we are using the idea that **momentum is conserved**; that is, when objects interact, for example in a collision, their momentum is shared between them. The total amount of momentum remains constant.

Questions

1 a On what two quantities does an object's momentum depend?

b What are the units of momentum?

2 Calculate the momentum of a car of mass 600 kg moving at 25 m/s.

3 A ball of mass 0.2 kg is moving at 3 m/s. It collides with a stationary ball of mass 0.1 kg. The two balls move off together at 2 m/s. Show that momentum is conserved in this collision. (Hint: Calculate the total momentum both before and after the collision; compare them.)

Summary

- The momentum of an object (in kg m/s) equals its mass (in kg) times its velocity (in m/s).

- When objects interact, momentum is conserved.

24:7 Explosive force

When a skyrocket explodes, brilliant sparks fly out in all directions. You would be surprised if most of the sparks went to the left and only a few to the right. In an explosion, equal amounts of momentum are created in opposite directions.

The symmetry of this explosion shows that momentum is conserved.

Explosions

When a gun is fired, the bullet flies off fast in one direction. The gun is pushed back (recoils) in the opposite direction, but much more slowly. In the diagram, the gun has a mass 1000 times greater than that of the bullet. The bullet flies off 1000 times as fast as the gun recoils.

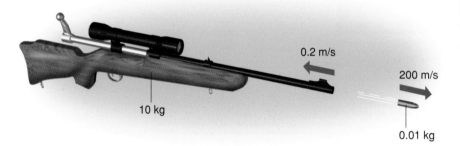

0.2 m/s

200 m/s

10 kg

0.01 kg

momentum of bullet = 0.01 kg × 200 m/s = 2 kg m/s to right

momentum of gun = 10 kg × 0.2 m/s = 2 kg m/s to left

Why is this? Before the trigger is pulled, both gun and bullet are stationary.

◆ momentum before explosion = 0 kg m/s

After the gun is fired, the gun and the bullet each have momentum, but in opposite directions. We will call the gun's momentum negative, because it is to the left.

◆ momentum after explosion = 2 kg m/s – 2 kg m/s = 0 kg m/s

So there is no more momentum after the explosion than before it. Momentum is *conserved* in the explosion. (Momentum is *always* conserved.)

a If the gun in this example had a mass of 20 kg, what would its speed of recoil be?

We can use this idea to solve problems involving explosions. The worked example shows how to use the relationship

momentum to left = momentum to right

Worked example

Two roller skaters are standing arguing. One pushes the other so that he moves backwards at 4 m/s. With what speed does the first skater recoil? (This might not sound much like an 'explosion', but we can apply the same idea.)

The diagram shows the masses and speeds of the skaters. For an explosion we can write:

momentum to left = momentum to right

With values from the diagram:

80 kg × v = 60 kg × 4 m/s

Rearranging gives

v = (60 kg × 4 m/s) / 80 kg = 4 m/s × 60 / 80 = 3 m/s

Not surprisingly, the heavier person recoils more slowly.

b Suppose one skater had twice the mass of the other. What could you say about their speeds?

Diagram for worked example.

Forces changing momentum

Why do *both* skaters move when one pushes the other? The big skater pushes the smaller one; an equal but opposite force pushes back on him.

Forces are also at work inside the gun. The explosive in the bullet provides a force that pushes the bullet forwards; an equal and opposite force pushes backwards on the gun.

A force is needed to change an object's momentum. The bigger the force, and the longer it acts for, the greater the change in momentum it produces. We can write this as:

change in momentum = force × time

or

$$\text{force} = \frac{\text{change in momentum}}{\text{time}}$$

c What are the units of each quantity in these equations?

force of bullet on gun   force of gun on bullet

Forces are always created in equal-and-opposite pairs. They act on different objects.

Questions

1 a Which produces a bigger change in momentum: a big force acting for a long time, or a small force acting for a short time?

   b Which produces a bigger change in momentum: a 100 N force acting for 10 s, or a 10 N force acting for 50 s?

2 A cannon of mass 5000 kg fires a shell of mass 20 kg. The shell leaves the cannon at 250 m/s. With what speed does the cannon recoil?

3 A car of mass 1000 kg is travelling at 20 m/s. The driver applies the brakes.

   a Calculate the momentum of the car.

   b The driver wants the car to stop in 10 s. What force must the brakes provide to do this?

Summary

- In explosions, momentum is conserved:

  momentum to left = momentum to right

- The force needed to produce a given change in momentum is given by:

  $$\text{force} = \frac{\text{change in momentum}}{\text{time}}$$

24:8 Collisions

When two cars collide, a force acts on each car. These forces are equal and opposite, just as in an explosion. The momentum of each car is changed as a result.

In a collision like this, each car feels the same force, acting for the same time. However, one car may be more badly affected than the other.

We can apply the idea of conservation of momentum to collisions, but the situation is slightly more complicated. We use the following equation:

total momentum = total momentum
before collision   after collision

The worked example shows how.

Worked example 1

A red ball of mass 5 kg, moving at 4 m/s, collides with a larger, stationary blue ball of mass 8 kg. The large ball moves off at 3 m/s. How does the first ball move after the collision? (Give direction and speed.)

Start by drawing a diagram to show how the balls move before and after the collision. We assume that the first ball continues to move at speed v to the right. Now we can say that:

total momentum = total momentum
before collision   after collision

Putting in values gives

$$(5\text{ kg} \times 4\text{ m/s}) + (8\text{ kg} \times 0\text{ m/s}) = (5\text{ kg} \times v) + (8\text{ kg} \times 3\text{ m/s})$$

$$20 = 5v + 24 \text{ (units omitted for clarity)}$$

$$v = -4/5 = -0.8\text{ m/s}$$

So the red ball moves at 0.8 m/s; the minus sign says that it bounces backwards (to the left). You might have guessed that a smaller object will bounce backwards when it collides with a bigger one.

a What would you expect to happen if the larger ball ran into the smaller one?

before collision

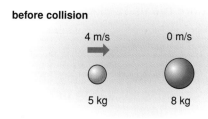

after collision

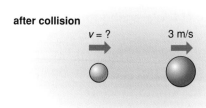

Before-and-after diagrams will help you solve collision problems.

Momentum and energy

Moving objects don't have just momentum; they also have kinetic energy. In an explosion, this energy might come from chemicals that burn rapidly (think of a firework) and transfer their energy to the objects, which move away.

In a collision between moving objects, the objects already have kinetic energy. There is no source of *extra* energy. Usually, some kinetic energy is lost in the collision – for example, as heat or sound. If two cars collide, a lot of kinetic energy is lost and the cars become badly deformed – it takes a lot of energy to deform a car. Less kinetic energy will be lost if the colliding objects are springy.

◆ If no kinetic energy is lost in a collision, it is described as an **elastic collision**.

◆ If some kinetic energy is transformed to other forms, the collision is **inelastic**.

> Remember – to calculate kinetic energy:
>
> $$\text{kinetic energy} = \tfrac{1}{2} \times \text{mass} \times (\text{speed})^2$$

Worked example 2

In a game of bowls, a 3 kg ball moving at 2 m/s collides with an identical stationary ball. The first ball stops dead; the second one moves off at 2 m/s in the same direction as the first ball. Is this collision elastic?

It isn't difficult to see that this is an elastic collision. Calculate the kinetic energies of the balls before and after the collision:

before collision: total KE $= [\tfrac{1}{2} \times 3\,\text{kg} \times (2\,\text{m/s})^2] + 0\,\text{J} = 6\,\text{J}$

after collision: total KE $= 0\,\text{J} + [\tfrac{1}{2} \times 3\,\text{kg} \times (2\,\text{m/s})^2] = 6\,\text{J}$

Since there is no change in total kinetic energy, the collision is elastic.

b Show that momentum is conserved in this collision.

before collision

2 m/s   0 m/s

3 kg   3 kg

after collision

0 m/s   2 m/s

3 kg   3 kg

Diagram for worked example 2.

Questions

1 A car of mass 800 kg is travelling at 20 m/s. It collides with a stationary car of mass 1200 kg; the two cars move off together. What is their combined speed? (Remember to draw a before-and-after diagram.)

2 Two identical snooker balls are moving at speeds of 2 m/s and 3 m/s when they collide head-on. The slower one bounces back at 1 m/s; how does the other one move? (Give its speed and direction.)

3 Look at worked example 1 on the opposite page. Calculate:

   a the kinetic energy of the red ball before the collision

   b the kinetic energies of the two balls after the collision. (Take care: calculate the KE of each ball separately.)

   c Is the collision elastic or inelastic?

4 In a game of bowls, a 3 kg ball moving at 3 m/s collides with an identical stationary ball. The second ball moves off at 2 m/s in the same direction as the first ball.

   a How fast does the first ball move after the collision, and in which direction?

   b Is this collision elastic?

Summary

• When objects collide, their total momentum before the collision equals their total momentum after the collision: momentum is *conserved*. This allows us to solve problems.

• No kinetic energy is lost in an *elastic* collision.

In the 1830s, Charles Darwin spent five years travelling around the world on board the *Beagle*. As well as studying the plants and animals in the countries he visited, he also made a study of geology. At that time, people were developing new theories about the origins of mountains and valleys.

Darwin climbed high up in the Andes mountain range of South America. When he had reached a height of over 5000 m above sea level, he examined some rocks. To his delight, he found that they contained fossilised sea-snails. What were these fossils doing so far from the sea?

Darwin believed that the mountains of South America were gradually rising upwards from the sea. He thought that this was a very slow process, taking millions of years. But other scientists had different ideas.

- Some believed that the Earth had once been very hot; as it cooled down, it contracted, and this caused the solid crust to wrinkle.

- Others, who believed the Bible literally, thought that the fossils were a proof of Noah's flood. They believed that the Earth was just 6000 years old.

Going up, going down

Darwin's novel idea was that, if some land was rising upwards, land elsewhere must be sinking. To test his idea, he looked for evidence of land sinking beneath the sea. And he found it.

As the *Beagle* crossed the Pacific Ocean, it called at some tiny islands. These atolls were little more than coral reefs, poking out of the sea. Darwin guessed that these were all that was left of ancient mountains, sinking beneath the waves. As a mountain sank, a coral reef formed. The further beneath the ocean surface the mountain sank, the higher grew the reef. Darwin used a plumb-line to check the depth of the ocean. He found that, just a short distance from an atoll, the sea was thousands of metres deep. This told him that he was indeed above an underwater mountain.

The *Beagle*, with Charles Darwin aboard, arrives off Tierra del Fuego.

This sedimentary rock, collected from a mountainside, contains fossilised sea creatures.

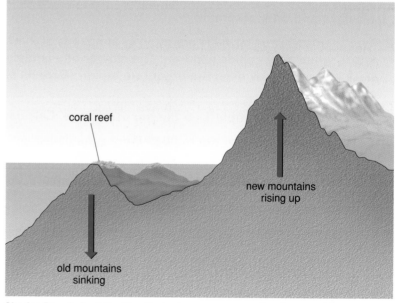

coral reef

new mountains rising up

old mountains sinking

Charles Darwin had the idea that when new mountains rise up, old mountains sink beneath the sea.

Undersea volcanoes

Today, we know a lot more about the structure of the sea-bed. Survey ships have used ultrasound to map its contours, and submarines have visited some of the deepest places. In the mid-Atlantic, a ridge of volcanoes can be detected. Alongside these are vents, where superheated water bubbles up from underground. This water contains sulphurous compounds that act as an energy source for a strange community of creatures – worms, crabs and fish of types we never see in our shallow seas.

This hot water is evidence of the hot interior of the Earth, which is heated by energy released by the decay of radioactive substances in the mantle and core.

Darwin had the idea that major changes might still be occurring in the rocks of the Earth's crust. He was right, but he couldn't imagine how much the Earth's surface has changed during the four and a half billion years of its existence. Today, we know about continental drift and the theory of **plate tectonics** that explains it. In Darwin's day, no-one had any idea of the possible mechanisms that could cause such great changes.

a You studied the theory of plate tectonics in the *Earth Materials* module. What is meant by a 'tectonic plate'?

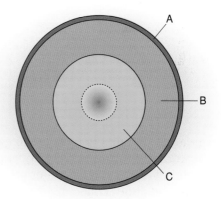

Questions

In the *Earth Materials* module, you learned about the structure of the Earth. These questions will help you recall what you learned then.

1 The diagram shows the internal structure of the Earth. Copy the diagram and name the parts labelled A, B and C. (You will find the names in the text above.)

2 Write short paragraphs describing each of the three layers named in question 1. Include each of the following phrases in your descriptions, relating them to the correct layer.

◆ a solid that can flow very slowly

◆ spherical, with radius slightly more than half the Earth's radius

◆ made of nickel and iron

◆ the densest layer

◆ reaches almost halfway to the centre of the Earth

◆ the thinnest and coolest layer

◆ mostly liquid but with a solid centre

Summary

- The Earth's surface is in a state of constant but very slow change.

- New mountain ranges are pushed upwards as older ones sink.

Alfred Wegener was a German scientist who developed a detailed theory of **continental drift**. On a visit to the Arctic island of Spitzbergen, he noticed that some of the rocks contained fossils of tropical ferns. His explanation was that Spitzbergen itself had slowly drifted up from the tropics.

a Wegener was a meteorologist – he studied the weather. What alternative explanation, connected with climate, might there be for tropical fossils in Arctic rocks?

Alfred Wegener, the German meteorologist who studied continental drift.

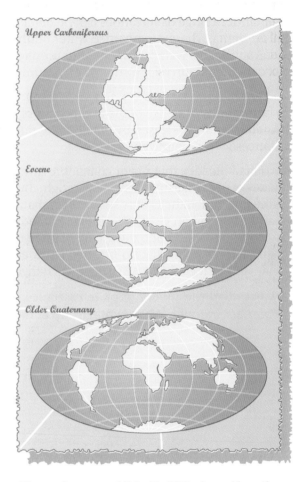

Wegener's maps, published in 1915, showed how the continents gradually separated over a period of 220 million years.

Collecting evidence

Wegener was not the first to have noted evidence for continental drift. Many others had noticed the good fit between the coastlines of Africa and South America. However, it was Wegener who set about collecting extensive evidence to show that these two continents might once have been joined. He found that rocks, fossils and vegetation showed almost identical patterns, despite the fact that the two landmasses were thousands of kilometres apart.

In 1928, a major conference of geologists considered his ideas, but they were laughed out of court. How could Australia, with a mass of one million million million tonnes, have drifted around the globe? Wegener's problem was that he could not explain how this could happen.

b In the 1920s, many geologists believed that the Atlantic Ocean was the hole formed when the Moon was ripped from the Earth by the pull of a passing star. Why do you think they could believe this, but they could not accept Wegener's ideas?

Attractive evidence

Wegener died in 1930. He did not live to see his theory gain acceptance. The new evidence that tipped the balance came from studies of the magnetism of rocks on the ocean bed.

Most rocks contain a certain amount of iron and other magnetic elements. When a molten rock solidifies, it retains a small amount of the Earth's magnetism from the time when it became solid. When survey ships examined the rocks forming the ocean beds, they discovered two things:

◆ First, some rocks were magnetised north–south, others south–north, suggesting that the Earth's magnetic field changes its direction from time to time. These changes are known as **magnetic reversals**.

◆ There was a remarkable pattern in the way the rocks are magnetised. Sailing a course across the North Atlantic, for example, they discovered that the rocks in the eastern half were a *mirror image* of those in the western half.

The explanation offered for these discoveries was that, in the middle of the ocean, new rocks are constantly rising up from deep inside the Earth. These gradually push the continents apart, at a rate of a few centimetres per year.

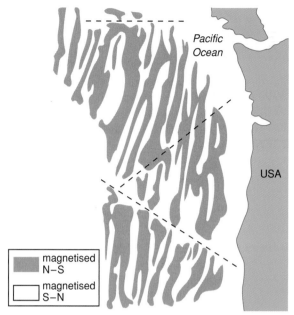

Pacific Ocean

USA

■ magnetised N–S
□ magnetised S–N

The pattern of magnetisation of rocks on the sea bed suggests that the Earth's magnetic field has undergone periodic reversals.

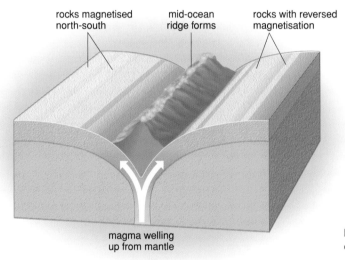

rocks magnetised north-south

mid-ocean ridge forms

rocks with reversed magnetisation

magma welling up from mantle

New rocks form where magma emerges beneath a mid-ocean ridge.

c Where would you look for the youngest rocks on the bed of the Atlantic Ocean? Where are the oldest rocks?

Questions

1 a Briefly outline Alfred Wegener's evidence that Africa and South America had once been in contact.

b What evidence might suggest that Australia is a continent which has not been in contact with any other landmass for a very long time? (Think about Australia's wildlife.)

2 New crust is forming along a huge ridge in the ocean bed all the way down the centre of the Atlantic – the mid-Atlantic ridge. This is giving rise to what is called 'sea floor spreading'. The Earth is not getting any bigger. What can you deduce from this?

Summary
• Initially, Wegener's theory of continental drift failed because he could not explain how giant land masses could move across the Earth's surface.

Today, we picture the Earth's lithosphere (the crust plus the top of the mantle) as being made up of many **tectonic plates**. These are solid chunks that move across the Earth's surface at a rate of a few centimetres per year.

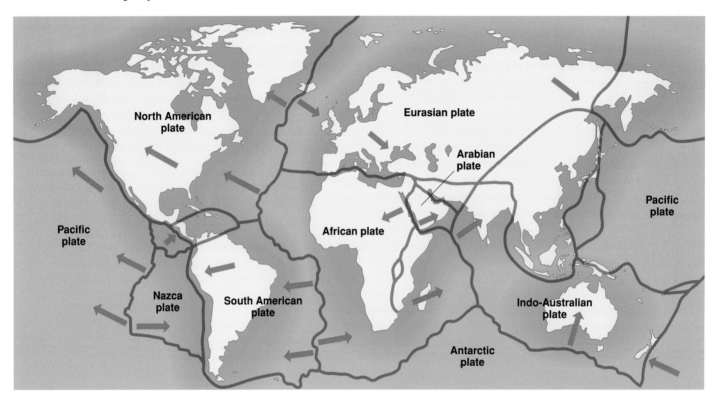

The Earth's major tectonic plates.

Up and under

The inside of the Earth is heated by the radioactive decay of elements in the core and mantle. This sets up giant convection currents in the mantle, which act as 'conveyor belts', moving the solid plates. In Wegener's day, no-one knew about this source of energy, so they could not imagine how continents could drift.

Even though plates move very slowly, they have enormous momentum. When they collide with each other, great forces result. This is what is happening, for example, in the Andes of South America, the mountain range about which Darwin speculated.

An oceanic plate beneath the eastern Pacific is colliding with the South American plate. The oceanic plate is denser, so it moves downwards under the less dense continental plate. This process is known as **subduction**. The continental plate is compressed and pushed upwards to form a mountain range.

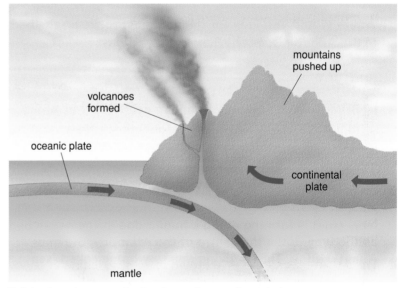

Subduction of an oceanic plate beneath a continental plate.

Where subduction occurs, great amounts of energy are released as the two plates scrape over one another. This leads to earthquakes. Volcanoes also form as molten magma pushes up through the continental crust.

a Explain Darwin's discovery of sea-snail fossils in the rocks high up in the Andes mountains.

Sliding past

California is famous for its earthquakes. Here, two plates are sliding slowly past one another. This does not result in volcanoes, but strong earthquakes are frequent.

As time passes, pressure builds up. A small earthquake may soon occur, or pressure may build for a long time, leading to a much bigger quake. The problem scientists have is in predicting what will trigger a quake to occur.

The aftermath of a major earthquake that struck Los Angeles in California in 1994.

b Why should the walker in the picture be worried?

Questions

1 What is meant by the lithosphere?

2 The diagram shows what happens where two plates are moving apart, as in the mid-Atlantic. Copy the diagram and:

 a add arrows to show how the plates are moving;

 b label the important features.

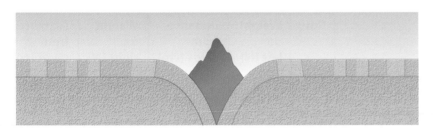

3 Look at the map at the top of the opposite page. The African plate is moving away from the Arabian plate to create the Red Sea. What would you expect to find under the middle of the Red Sea?

4 The Atlantic Ocean is 3000 km wide. It is widening at a rate of about 6 cm per year. Use this information to estimate the time it has taken for Europe and America to separate.

Summary
- The Earth's lithosphere is divided into separate tectonic plates.
- Natural radioactive decay heats the mantle; this results in convection currents that move the plates around.
- Separating plates result in oceans; colliding plates produce mountain ranges.

End of module questions

1 Three boys are playing on a seesaw. One sits on each end, while the third stands at the middle, above the pivot.

weight = 600 N

weight = 500 N

weight = 800 N

2.5m

2.5m

Calculate the moment of each boy's weight about the pivot.

2 A rope is being used to open a heavy trapdoor, as shown in the diagram.

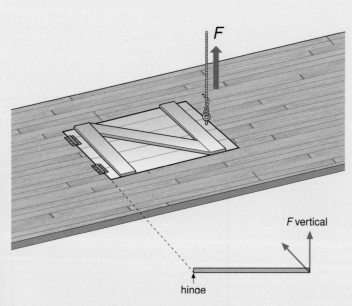

F

F vertical

hinge

Explain why a smaller force is required when the rope is vertical than when the rope is at an angle to the vertical.

3 A girl has made a Christmas decoration from a piece of card. She pins it to the window frame. The decoration hangs freely from the pin.

a Explain why the decoration hangs with its centre of mass directly below the pin.

b The girl pushes the decoration slightly to one side. Explain why the decoration swings downwards, towards its original position.

4 A pupil is investigating the turning effect of forces. He balances a metre rule at its midpoint, and places weights on either side.

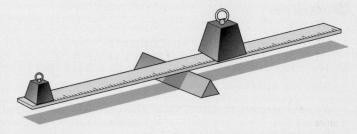

Row	Weight on left (N)	Distance from pivot (cm)	Weight on right (N)	Distance from pivot (cm)
A	5	20	10	10
B	10	20	25	10
C	15	20	10	30

a The table shows his results. Unfortunately, one row includes an incorrect reading. Which is it?

b Describe how the pupil could adapt the experiment to determine the weight of the metre rule. Include a diagram in your answer.

5 A hydrogen atom consists of a positively charged proton and a negatively charged electron. We can picture the electron orbiting around the proton. A centripetal force is needed to keep the electron in its orbit.

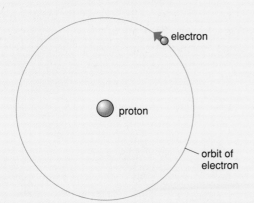

a What force provides this centripetal force?

b Copy the diagram and add an arrow to show the direction of this force on the electron.

6 A girl of mass 60 kg is riding a bicycle of mass 20 kg along a road at a speed of 10 m/s.

a Calculate the total momentum of the girl and her bike.

b Ahead, traffic lights turn red. The girl applies the brakes. If the bike is to stop within 2 s, what force must the brakes provide?

7 A game of bowls is played with identical balls of mass 5 kg. A ball moving at 2 m/s collides with a stationary ball. The second ball moves off at 1.5 m/s. The first ball continues at 0.5 m/s.

before collision   **after collision**

2 m/s   0.5 m/s   1.5 m/s

a Explain what it means to say that momentum is conserved in a collision like this.

b By means of a suitable calculation, show that momentum is conserved in this collision.

c Explain what is meant by an *elastic* collision.

d By means of a suitable calculation, show that this collision is *not* elastic.

8 We picture the Earth's lithosphere as being cracked into a number of tectonic plates. These move slowly over the Earth's surface.

a What is meant by the Earth's *lithosphere*?

b A tectonic plate has a mass of millions of millions of tonnes. Explain how such a massive object is moved.

9 The diagram shows some of the tectonic plates that make up the Earth's surface.

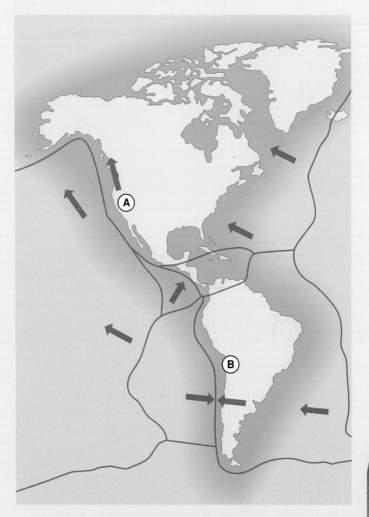

a Explain why earthquakes occur at point A, on the coast of California.

b Explain why a mountain range (the Andes) is forming at point B.

Extended homework questions

1 The diagram shows a wooden rod hanging freely from a pivot. Two forces act on the rod: its weight *W*, and the upward force *F* of the pivot.

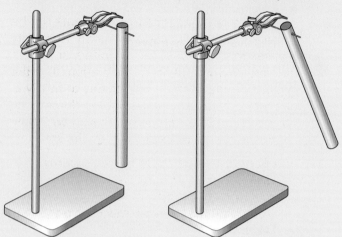

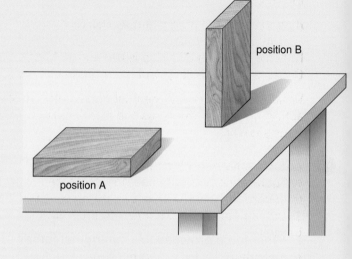

position B

position A

a The rod hangs straight down from the pivot. Draw a diagram showing the rod and the forces acting on it.
b Explain why, in this position, the weight of the rod does not exert any turning effect on it.
c The rod is pulled gently to the side, as shown. Draw a diagram to show the forces that now act on the rod, and explain why, when the rod is released, it will start to swing back to its previous position.

2 **a** A small child is playing with some wooden blocks on a table. She pushes one block towards the edge of the table (diagram below). Eventually, it tips over and falls to the floor. Using the idea of *centre of mass*, explain why this happens.

b The child enjoys standing a rectangular block on end, and then pushing it so that it topples over. Referring to the diagram above, explain why the block is more stable in position A than in position B.

3 A metre rule weighing 5 N is pivoted at its 40 cm mark. The diagram shows two ways in which it can be balanced at this point: by pushing downwards at the 0 cm mark, or pushing upwards at the 100 cm mark. Calculate each of the forces required to do this.

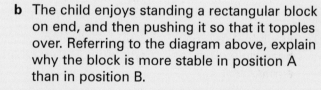

40 cm

4 The Moon travels around the Earth in an orbit that is (almost) circular.

a Explain why a force is needed to keep it in its orbit.
b What provides this force?
c Why is this force described as a *centripetal force*?

5 When athletes race around a circular track, they need a centripetal force to keep them following the curve of the track. To produce this force, they lean 'into the bend'.

Three runners are following each other around the track.

A is in the lead; he has a mass of 70 kg and is running at 10 m/s.
B has a mass of 65 kg and is running at 10 m/s.
C has a mass of 65 kg and is running at 9 m/s.

Which runner has the greatest centripetal force acting on him? Which has the least? Explain your answers.

6 At a motor vehicle test station, vehicles are deliberately crashed to see how they stand up to severe impacts. In one test, a bus of mass 15 000 kg collides at 22 m/s into a concrete barrier.

a Calculate the bus's momentum.
b The collision lasts 1.1 seconds. Calculate the average force acting on the bus during this time.

7 In a lab experiment, a moving trolley collides head-on with a stationary trolley. Each trolley has a mass of 1 kg.

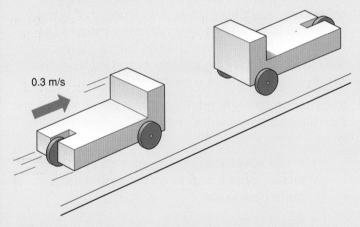

0.3 m/s

a As they collide, each trolley exerts a force on the other. What can you say about these two forces?
b The first trolley is moving at 0.3 m/s when it strikes the second trolley. What is its momentum? What is its kinetic energy?

c The two trolleys stick together. At what speed do they move after the collision?
d Could this collision be described as elastic? Support your answer with an appropriate calculation.
e The experiment is repeated with one change: the mass of the second trolley is increased to 2 kg. With what speed will the trolleys move off after they join together?

8 An astronaut is engaged in repair work on the outside of an orbiting space station. Suddenly he realises that his tether has snapped, and he is floating slowly away from the station. In order to get back to the station, he decides to throw a spanner out into space. Using the idea of conservation of momentum, explain why this will cause him to move back towards the station.

9 The Earth's crust is made of rocks whose average density is much less than the average density of the Earth as a whole. What does this tell you about the material making up the mantle and core?

10 Alfred Wegener developed the theory of continental drift in the early years of the twentieth century. It was not generally accepted for over 50 years.

a Explain what is meant by 'continental drift'.
b What evidence did Wegener have to support his theory?
c Why did it take so long for his theory to become accepted?

11 When two *tectonic plates* collide, an oceanic plate may be *subducted* under a continental plate. The oceanic plate then partially melts. The continental plate is compressed, leading to folding, faulting and *metamorphism*. *Magma* may rise up through the continental crust.

a Explain what is meant by each of the terms in *italics*.
b What is the result when magma breaks through the crust?
c What other phenomenon might occur where one plate is subducted beneath another?

Recap material

Getting materials to cells
Large insoluble food molecules are digested into soluble substances so that they can be absorbed into the bloodstream. The breakdown of large molecules into smaller molecules is speeded up by enzymes.

The circulatory system transports substances around the body. Red blood cells transport oxygen from the lungs to the organs. Plasma transports:

- soluble products of digestion from the small intestine to other organs
- carbon dioxide from the organs to the lungs
- waste urea from the liver to the kidneys.

Releasing energy
Energy is released during aerobic respiration that takes place in the mitochondria of cells. When there is a shortage of oxygen, cells may carry out anaerobic respiration. This releases waste lactic acid. The energy released during respiration is used:

- to build larger molecules from smaller ones
- to enable muscles to contract
- to maintain a steady body temperature
- in the active transport of substances.

Using energy from the Sun
Green plants can make food using photosynthesis, which is summarised as:

Carbon dioxide + water + (light energy) → glucose + oxygen

Carbon dioxide enters and leaves cells by diffusing from a higher to a lower concentration.

During photosynthesis:

- light energy is absorbed by chlorophyll which is found in the chloroplasts in some plant cells
- this energy is used to convert carbon dioxide and water into glucose
- oxygen is released as a by-product.

The glucose produced may be converted into insoluble starch for storage. Plant cells use some of the glucose produced during photosynthesis for respiration.

Removing waste
Humans need to remove waste and keep the conditions inside their bodies constant. Waste products that have to be removed include:

- carbon dioxide produced by respiration
- urea produced in the liver by the breakdown of excess amino acids; urea is then removed by the kidneys in urine which collects in the bladder.

Controlling conditions
The kidneys help to keep the conditions in the body constant by:

- filtering the blood
- reabsorbing all the glucose
- reabsorbing dissolved ions needed by the body
- reabsorbing the water needed by the body
- removing urea, excess ions and excess water.

Many processes in the body are controlled by chemicals called hormones. The amount of water in the blood is controlled by a hormone called ADH which is released by the pituitary gland. Glucose and dissolved ions may be actively absorbed from the kidney tubules against a concentration gradient.

Body temperature is monitored and controlled by the thermoregulatory centre in the brain. If the core temperature is too high:

- blood vessels supplying the skin capillaries dilate: more blood flows through them and more heat is lost
- sweat glands release more sweat which cools the body as it evaporates.

Moving and feeding
Vertebrates have an internal skeleton which provides the framework for support and movement. Bones are rigid to support the body and for muscle attachment. Muscle contraction only moves bones at a joint.

- Fish have adaptations for swimming and birds have adaptations for flight.
- Mammals have teeth and jaws and digestive systems suited to their method of feeding.
- Mussels feed by filtering microscopic plankton found in water.

- Mosquitoes have mouthparts adapted to suck blood from capillaries. Aphids, houseflies and butterflies feed by sucking fluids into their mouths.

Recap questions

1 The table shows the units of lactic acid produced in the muscles of an athlete during a 200 m race.

Time (seconds)	0	5	10	15	20	25	30	35
Lactic acid units	0	2	8	25	38	30	25	18

  a Name the process which produces lactic acid.

  b Explain why lactic acid was produced in the athlete's muscles during the race.

  c Explain what happens to the lactic acid after the race.

2 The table shows the concentration of substances in different regions. (All the values are in mg per litre.)

Substance	Blood entering kidney	Kidney tubule	Urine
Urea	0.5	25	25
Glucose	1.5	1.5	0
Protein	50.0	0	0

  a Which organ in the body produces urea?

  b What is urea produced from?

  c Which substances pass from the blood into the kidney tubule?

  d Explain why glucose is present in the kidney tubule and not in urine.

3 The graph shows the amount of sweat and urine produced by a person at different temperatures.

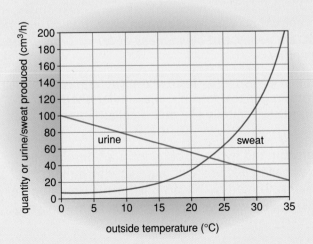

  a At what temperature is the amount of sweat and urine the same?

  b Explain why the amount of sweat produced increases as temperature increases.

  c i Describe how temperature affects urine production.

    ii Explain why the amount of urine produced changes as temperature changes.

4 **a** Copy and complete the following equation which summarises photosynthesis.

    Carbon + _____ → glucose + _____
    dioxide

  b In addition to the substances shown in the equation, what else is needed for photosynthesis?

  c Explain how plants use the glucose produced by photosynthesis.

5 The table below shows the number of red blood cells of people living at different heights above sea level. The air at higher levels contains less oxygen.

Height above sea level (metres)	Number of red cells per mm³
0	5000
1500	6500
5500	7400

  a How many more red cells are present in each mm³ of blood at 5500 m compared to sea level?

  b Explain why the increase in the number of red cells benefits people living in mountainous regions.

  c Describe how oxygen moves from the alveoli in the lungs to red blood cells.

Why is water so important?

Water is the most abundant chemical on the Earth's surface and is essential for life. It is widely used in industry as a solvent and as a coolant. It is also an important raw material with many uses, including the manufacture of sulphuric acid.

Water containing dissolved calcium or magnesium compounds is called *hard water*. This is formed when natural waters flow over the ground or rocks. Hard water can be softened by removing these compounds. Adding sodium carbonate solution precipitates out calcium carbonate or magnesium carbonate. Ion exchange columns contain hydrogen or sodium ions which replace calcium and magnesium ions when hard water passes through.

Most *ionic* compounds are soluble in water, whilst most *covalent* compounds are insoluble in water.

The *solubility* of a solute in water, or any other solvent, is usually given in grams of solute per 100 grams of water (or solvent) at that temperature.

Most solutes become more soluble as the temperature increases. A *saturated* solution will not dissolve any more of the solute at that temperature. When a hot saturated solution cools, some of the solute separates from the solution, often forming crystals.

You will need to be able to interpret solubility curves and use them to explain crystallisation.

Why do acids and alkalis behave as they do?

Acids and alkalis only show their properties in water. Acids, in aqueous solution, produce H^+ ions (the H^+ ion is just a proton). These become hydrated (joined with water) and are shown as H^+ (aq). Alkalis, in aqueous solution, produce OH^- ions which can 'mop up' H^+ ions. Because of this, acids are called *proton donors*, whilst bases are *proton acceptors*.

You will need to know how Arrhenius, Lowry and Brønsted helped to develop our ideas about acid–base reactions. You will also need to be able to explain why the work of Arrhenius took much longer to be accepted than that of Lowry and Brønsted.

The strength of an acid or alkali depends on how much it is ionised in water. Hydrochloric, sulphuric and nitric acids are strong acids, and sodium and potassium hydroxides are strong alkalis, because they show 100% ionisation in aqueous solution.

Weak acids such as ethanoic, citric and carbonic acids, or weak alkalis such as ammonia solution, are only partially ionised in water.

Strong acids have very low pH and react vigorously with metals such as zinc. Strong alkalis have very high pH (up to 14). Weak acids and alkalis at the same concentration have pH closer to 7 (neutral).

How much will react?

The volume of acid and alkali solutions which neutralise each other can be measured by titration using a suitable indicator. This can be used to find the concentration of an acid or alkali from the relative volumes used and the concentration of one of the two reactants.

The concentration of an aqueous solution is usually expressed in moles per cubic decimetre ($mol\ dm^{-3}$) (M). The relative atomic mass of an element or the relative formula mass of a compound in grams is equal to one *mole* of that substance.

You should be able to calculate the number of moles given relative atomic or formula masses, or to calculate the mass of a substance in a given mole quantity.

You should also be able to perform molar calculations involving solutions including neutralisation reactions (where the balanced chemical equation is given).

What are organic compounds and how can we use them?

Coal, crude oil, natural gas and wood contain compounds built around carbon chains. Such compounds are called *organic* compounds. When they are burned in plenty of air, the carbon is oxidised to carbon dioxide and the hydrogen is oxidised to water.

If the supply of air is restricted, incomplete combustion occurs, forming carbon monoxide and/or carbon. Carbon monoxide is poisonous because it interferes with the way blood carries oxygen. Organic compounds such as plastics that contain chlorine and nitrogen produce additional poisonous fumes when burnt.

You should be able to use given data to compare the cost, efficiency and cleanliness of burning different fossil fuels.

Organic compounds form chemical *families* with a common general formula and similar chemical properties. A family like this is called a *homologous series*.

The saturated hydrocarbons form a homologous series called *alkanes* with a general formula C_nH_{2n+2}. The unsaturated hydrocarbons form a homologous series called *alkenes* with a general formula C_nH_{2n}.

Index